The Tipping Points

GW00584812

Acknowledgement

Painting on the front cover
See Saw by Leonard Creo
What do you see in the painting on the cover of this book? Children happy at play, a young boy assisting two girls to have a better see saw ride or a disruptive boy ruining the play of his friends? Maybe you can see all three explanations and more, and perhaps therein lies an explanation of how difficult ADHD is to understand; we all see things differently and have varying levels of tolerance. This picture, by the acclaimed artist Leonard Creo, entitled 'See Saw', epitomises the ADHD debate. I am in Leonard's debt for allowing me the right to use his painting as my cover for this work; that he is excited about this as I am is a measure of a truly special man.

'See Saw' – used with kind permission of the artist Leonard Creo.

The Tipping Points

What professionals should recognise as the social impact of ADHD

Phil Anderton PhD

With a foreword by
Roger Graef OBE

Published by

ADDiSS
ADHD INFORMATION SERVICES
Registered Charity No: 1070827

Published in the UK in November 2007 by

ADD Information Services Ltd
2nd floor, Premier House
112 Station Road
Edgware
Middlesex
HA8 7BJ
Email: info@addiss.co.uk
Website www.addiss.co.uk

Imprint
ADDISS

British Library Cataloguing in publication dtata.
A catalogue record for this book is available from the British Library

ISBN 978-0-9554033-2-3

Disclaimer;
The information presented in this book is intended to educate and provide a source of general information and support. It is not intended as a substitute for a medical diagnosis or treatment.

Cover design by Braden Threadgold Design Agency
Typset by Hope Services (Abingdon) Ltd.
Printed and bound in the UK by Biddles Ltd, King's Lynn, Norfolk

About the author

Phillip Anderton (PhD) served as a police officer for over 27 years and in 2007 embarked on a second career as a management consultant. After a full operational career the later stages of his police service saw him rise to senior and more strategic roles. He specialised in diversity, youth issues, training and performance management. His final responsibilities were for the Home Office, managing change throughout the service in the UK in relation to intelligence sharing and information exchanges.

Phil's interest in ADHD was borne out of his responsibilities in Lancashire (UK) for youth crime and mental health issues. Working with a colleague, Steve Brown, on the premise that prevention concepts in youth crime had a long way to go before they became totally effective, Phil began researching mental health disorders and in particular ADHD. He now works alongside ADDISS as their criminal justice advisor, and assists organisations across Europe and speaks internationally on this subject. In 2002 he was the Crime Concern Problem Solver of the Year as a result of his crime reduction successes in Lancashire. Phil has a PhD from Hull University which focused on performance management through individual competence in the workplace.

He lives in northern England with his wife Clare and daughter Olivia.

Foreword

As a film producer I have studied human behaviour for a considerable part of my life, through research, filming 'fly on the wall' documentaries or when writing my own books. Some of the most interesting experiences during this work have come from observing the many men and women who form our police service.

Policing society has been and remains a dynamic and challenging environment for anyone to work in, whether in the front line on the streets or in a position of management and strategic decision making. One of the more influential developments over recent times has been the acceptance amongst society that 'policing', by which I mean maintaining law and order, is no longer the sole responsibility of the police; many different people from diverse organisations now perform that role, together. This unity of task is of paramount importance when we consider the issues raised in this book.

By examining a root cause of some of the problems within this cohort of our society, and dealing with that in an informed manner, this book asserts that the negative social outcomes that face many young people can be avoided. It is right to make that assertion. The compelling research undertaken by the author found that the most dominant cause of young people's entry into the criminal justice system is the near total misunderstanding of lower level mental health disorders such as Attention Deficit Hyperactivity Disorder (ADHD).

This work has proven to be ground-breaking and inspirational for those professionals lucky enough to have worked with Phil Anderton, especially those who deal with young people in the course of their everyday lives. Those who have responsibilities for keeping children on a straight and narrow path, away from the criminal justice system, have frequently changed the way they carry out their responsibilities after workshops on the subject that he facilitated.

This book is the culmination of Phil's research and work in the UK, Europe and the States where demand for his activities and thoughts to be published has been high.

'The Tipping Points' takes the reader through the issues of ADHD from describing it in the context of bringing about social outcomes, through an introduction to the mindset needed to solve problems, to the specific issues of ADHD for children growing up, and culminates with a detailed analysis of the locations of the tipping points in a young persons life.

The book is deliberately not written as academic text and it is an easy read for people who are, or who want to be, interested in the subject. There are no comparative books in this arena and as such the book is unique in the way it grounds medical and academic science into a book that has a clearly defined outcome focus.

The book will appeal to audiences from all nations. The author's experience of speaking throughout Europe and the United States confirms the unique nature of the text.

I am one of the lucky few, my ADHD is a gift for me, I have managed to 'survive' and I have a lifestyle that I have carved to suit me. Not everyone has the opportunities I have had. For many, the subjects of this book, ADHD is a debilitating disorder. I commend this book to all professionals who work with children, it is our collective responsibility to increase the opportunities for the young children and adolescents around us, this book definitely assists us to do that.

Roger Graef OBE
Filmmaker, broadcaster and criminologist.

Table of contents

Acknowledgements   xi

Chapter One: Introduction   1
  Why ADHD   2
  Social norms   3
  Kids of the cone   5

Chapter two: Problem solving   9
  SARA   10
  PAT   11

Chapter three: What is ADHD?   15
  An easy way to understand what ADHD is for lay people   15
  The medically based way of describing ADHD   17
  Diagnosing ADHD   19
  DSM IV criteria for ADHD (abridged)   20
  Co-morbid conditions   21
  Myths about ADHD   22

Chapter four: ADHD and crime   25
  Longitudinal studies of criminal behaviour   26
  Vulnerability and increased risk   26
  Coping strategies for potential young offenders   28

Chapter five: ADHD and crime—the statistics   31

Chapter six: ADHD and outcomes   33
  Outcomes in adult life   33
  Executive functions   34
  Progressive behavioural patterns   41

Chapter seven: ADHD and problematic drug use   43
  Relationship models for ADHD and problematic substance use   46
  Self-medication   48
  Treatment regimens   51
  Treatment models   52

Chapter eight: ADHD and road use   55
  Driving and ADHD   56
  Encouraging safer driving   57

Chapter nine: Tipping points   61

Appendices   65
   Appendix 1—Myths about ADHD   65
   Appendix 2—Scarlett's story   71
   Appendix 3—ADHD and driving—advice for parents   73
   Appendix 4—Advice specifically for police officers regarding ADHD 75
   Appendix 5—Advice for magistrates court staff   77

Acknowledgements

This book represents a labour of love for me. I first really came into the professional world of ADHD when Andrea Bilbow was kind enough to find a place for me at a conference where Dr Rob Doyle was speaking about adults with ADHD. This was in Worcester and it was where I first met Annie Creo, a lady who makes a tremendously positive impression on every person she meets, as she did with me.

These three aforementioned people, Andrea, Rob and Annie personify everything that goes unsaid about working with ADHD. The endless hours of travelling, learning and assisting others to learn about the disorder often go unrecognised. Without their kindness, assistance and encouragement I would never have persevered with my work in this field. Professionally, I dedicate this book to them and all that they stand for, as a representation of the countless others in their field that have assisted me to come this far with my understanding.

The case studies used in this book are true life stories, of real people. There is a saying in the police that every touch leaves a trace. Each and every one of the people I have met during these working years have done this, and in so doing, have left a permanent memory for me. Not least of which, and singled out because she was the first to share her hardship with me, is Scarlett, an American whose heartfelt story touched my heart, as well as those we were able to share it with via BBC radio in 2004.

When I announced that I was retiring from the police at the ADDISS conference in 2007 a young man took me to one side. He told me of his criminal convictions, his time on drugs and his spells in prison, and of his ADHD. He shook me by the hand and informed me that he was proud to know me, proud of the work that had been done and that singularly, I was the only copper he had any time for.

I sincerely dedicate this book to him and all those like him. Unless us professionals get our 'act together' and understand ADHD and people like him, boys and girls, men and women, will continue to enter the criminal justice system, unfairly, and completely misunderstood. Surely people who are poorly deserve better.

Throughout this work I was indebted to Steve Brown, and I always will be.

Finally a personal dedication, to my family without whose support I would never have had the wherewithal to undertake this work, and to Dave who consistently encouraged me, right from the start; he is missed.

Phil Anderton
May 2007

Chapter One

Introduction

MY WORK with Attention Deficit Hyperactivity Disorder (ADHD) began in late 2003. I was working as a police inspector and I had responsibilities for crime reduction, young people's issues and diversity across the county of Lancashire. The appointment of Steve Brown as my sergeant brought a new way of thinking into the office and as is it often said, he was a 'breath of fresh air'. Steve had a focus on youth crime and together we decided that we had a great opportunity to tackle this 'differently' aside from the usual advice to teenagers about drugs and the perils of shoplifting, we wanted to see if there was a new way of reducing the amount of young people in the criminal justice system.

We laboured long and hard to find something that hadn't been done already, the usual subjects had been well covered by peers across the UK, but then we stumbled across mental health, in particular, what we termed lower level mental health disorders. There was every chance that issues such as autism, foetal alcohol syndrome and ADHD had links into the kind of work we were seeking to carry out. Our self-created task was to identify if there were links, and if there were, to see if we could do anything about them.

The following text, written for the practitioner, outlines my findings, my thoughts and work to date. Each separate chapter outlines a unique perspective on ADHD within the overall context of the criminal justice system, and the book uses some case studies that amplify the thinking behind this work.

There are a number of facts about ADHD that I recommend are grounded before you, the reader, go any further:

1   Although nearly everyone I have met has an opinion on ADHD and believes they 'know all about it', normally they don't, and popular opinion has been formed from tabloids and daytime television chat shows. Please be prepared to have your perceptions of this debilitating disorder challenged from the outset.
2   **ADHD is real**, it is not caused by poor parenting, coloured sweets or poor diet. ADHD is a recognised mental health disorder and as such, professionals should be better informed, act appropriately and deliver services to young people with ADHD to the best of their abilities. To that end, leave your misconceptions at the door and enter a whole new world, a world where ADHD can and does destroy people's lives.

3 The purpose of this book is not to get you to assist the police to reduce crime, moreover, the purpose of this book is to allow adults working with young people with ADHD a greater chance of understanding the children they are responsible for. Should that happen, rather than reducing crime, which was my initial and simplistic initial goal, we will all stand a greater chance of giving those young people in our care more chance of achieving their life potential. Surely that is good enough reason to read this book and treat ADHD with an open mind?

Why ADHD

Fighting crime has a TV image, maybe for older readers, 'Dixon of Dock Green', for younger readers 'The Bill' or 'Life on Mars' form the terms of reference for policing. Over my 25 years as a police officer one factor changed beyond all recognition, that being, that crime reduction was no longer the sole responsibility of the police service. Legislation, for example the Crime and Disorder Act, ways and methods of working, such as problem solving in partnership, and the extension of the police family to include unsworn patrolling officers have all played their part in changing the shape of 'policing' in the 21st century.

Therefore, traditional methods of working have been challenged, the techniques taught in the 1980s are not all relevant in the modern day. The relationships between the public and the police are different and innovation really needs to satisfy the more up-to-date agenda. Working with ADHD offers opportunities in these areas. As I explore in the book, improvements in how we work with ADHD need people from different occupations to work together, these people need to see their activities from a fresh perspective, we all need to embrace every chance we have to get things right and, importantly, we need to work with carers and parents as well as the young people of the target audience.

ADHD has a very strong genetic component; some say it is as genetically disposed as height! Therefore, if two parents have ADHD there is a greater than 80% chance that their children will have it. We expect tall people to have tall children; we should similarly have an expectation that parents with ADHD will have children with ADHD. Putting this into a setting of realism, where we have kids that are struggling with their behaviour due to their ADHD, and some may look at the parents and say it is all their fault, then maybe, just maybe, it is, because they have ADHD too. No longer can we allow professionals to sit in judgement and say 'there's nothing wrong with him or her, it's the way he has been brought up'. Now we should challenge those opinion makers and see what support the whole family needs to ascertain what we can do to make the home a better place by understanding the family's issues, not just those of an unruly child.

Of course no writer or researcher has ever suggested that all 'bad' behaviour is caused by a genetic component; there are times when all young people misbehave. My suggestion is that for the 5% of our population that have ADHD, and that is a conservative estimate, it is a real problem; we do not observe behaviour of choice, we see behaviour where there isn't a choice. ADHD is pervasive across the whole of their life, but, and this is the powerful but, if ADHD is understood and managed appropriately, *we* can make a difference to the lives of those people who suffer.

For some, having ADHD is a gift. Some musicians, artists and entrepreneurs who have suffered a previous lack of acceptance amongst peers, and a lack of ability to regulate their behaviour suddenly find themselves 'fitting in' to a new way of working. Those I have spoken with would suggest that this is because their new lifestyle in the arts actually requires unprecedented creativity, freedom of thought and energy. These people are the lucky few, for many do not find their niche, the profession that suits them, many struggle through unemployment, hard times and financial and emotional hardships. It is the debate over lifestyle and social norms that start the introduction to this book on ADHD and its social outcomes.

Social norms

Many observers of the apparent rise in ADHD comment that 'it's that new thing', that 'it's just come about since the drug companies became involved', and some ask 'where were all these people before?'

ADHD isn't new; there is very strong evidence that people have had behavioural problems for many, many years. The labels may have changed, the diagnosis has gotten more sophisticated, but ADHD is not new. There are some facts though that I believe have allowed society to see more ADHD than previously, and although the prevalence has not increased, the apparent prevalence may have.

Let's briefly examine schooling. Generations ago, children went to school and were taught differently. There were segregated educational streams based on apparent ability, grammar schools for the academics, and technical colleges for those who preferred a more vocational educational style. Classrooms were managed differently, individual desks, regimented time management to the school bell, hard physical punishment for dissenters and the school leaving age was lower than the current UK initial exit point of 16 years.

School was all about the child, now we have league tables, performance targets, and it is questionable if the external focus is still all about children's individual needs and attainment.

For all children, especially for those with ADHD, behaviour was more controlled, motivation was high, whether by fear of punishment or because the educational stream was more suited, the facts were that schooling stood less chance of highlighting a child's ADHD than the present system.

Modern day students are all expected to study to academic levels in common ways, exams are frequent, and school performance some argue outweighs the needs of the child. Desks are shared by groups, distractions are many, discipline is more relaxed, perhaps based on self-discipline rather than an imposed regime, and children stay at school until a minimum age of 16.

Previous generations of children walked or cycled to school, often having long and physically challenging journeys at the beginning and end of the school day. For most school children of today, that exertion has been reduced if not removed. School buses, parents' cars and more local facilities have all served to reduce the physical effort required to get a child to the 21st century educational establishment. As we will see later, one of the natural methods of 'controlling' ADHD symptoms is the regular use of physical exercise; it's simple but it works.

This brief examination of education suggests therefore that although the base rate of inherent ADHD has not raised, changes in schooling techniques may have a part to play in observed behavioural disorders such as ADHD rising to the surface.

Employment opportunities also have a part to play. Gone are the days of UK based sweated industries such as ship building and car manufacturing, jobs that were followed through families, where physical exertion was the everyday norm. The manufacturing base of the UK is now based around the white coat industries of silicon, computers and chemicals and service based employment is more common than previously observed. Where troublesome youths would follow dad into the 'yard', those options are no longer available. Where unacceptable workplace behaviour of the past, bad language, fighting or rudeness was dealt with in a 'like on like' manner, the modern day manifestation of such traits leads to termination of contracts, tribunals and other punitive coping mechanisms.

Neither the examination of the school or the workplace environment should be seen as a desire to return to old style values. But what is apparent is that from many different angles, the apparent rise in ADHD can be justifiably explained through examinations of our changing and developing social structures. These debates give rise to the desperate need for higher skills within our workforces of professionals that have responsibility for children. The skills base of old is no longer relevant, people have changed, the social environment has changed and these developments have exposed failings in teacher training, social worker protocols, prison systems and police officers' methods of working. Not least of which, the ADHD agenda is one that requires changes, developments in new practices and an alternative mindset from those that persist from the previous generations.

ADHD has not become more of a problem in terms of numbers, professional skills have become less adept at dealing with the needs of society, which have changed and moved on. The burning question for any teacher, social worker, police officer, magistrate etc is, 'having heard this can **you** make the necessary changes'?

Kids of the cone

For a lot of people with attention problems, words and complicated documents can often present a major challenge, the ability to concentrate through long PowerPoint slides or written documents just isn't there. For this reason I endeavour to use diagrams and pictures as much as possible in presentations to audiences learning about ADHD, and I can see no reason to change that successful formula in this book.

In discussions with a colleague at a conference in the US, I was debating the need for a graphic representation of the issues around ADHD and the criminal justice system and together we came up with the 'kids of the cone' pictorial representation.

When we are born we all have many opportunities ahead of us, the world can literally be, our 'oyster', as we progress through our lives those chances

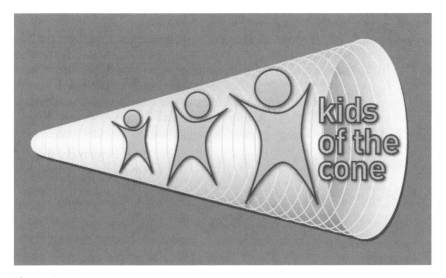

Figure 1

for development and success increase, and we move, for some rapidly, towards the wider end of the cone of life, where we can broaden out, challenge ourselves, develop and seek to achieve our birth given potential. Along the way, represented in the diagram by concentric rings, many people give us a helping hand. They may be teachers, social workers, ministers, police officers or whoever, the list is long.

Each one of those concentric rings is what we call a 'key contact opportunity', a chance for the people who can assist us to help us to achieve our potential, to get things right for us. But what if those people do not understand us? What if at each key contact opportunity, these people get things wrong for us? What if a pattern emerges, that every time we interact as a child, with teachers, social workers etc we are grossly misunderstood, and this continues time after time? My suggestion is that when this does occur, as it does for many young people with ADHD, the systematic failure to get things right leads to an alternative trajectory for those young people. As the cone gets larger towards its widest point, the opportunities get less and less but the risks of falling foul of the system become greater, those risks being, predominantly, risks of entering into the criminal justice system and being demonised.

The thinking behind this model leads me to forming an overriding hypothesis, a belief about why we need to work with ADHD. That hypothesis is:

> Each key contact an agency has with a child or young person who has ADHD is an opportunity to get things right. If we get this wrong we will systematically destroy that young person's chance of achieving their life potential.

We should be under no illusions at this point. Once a young person is in the criminal system, it is very hard to successfully get them out. Rehabilitation and the total cleansing of stigma are very arduous and difficult to achieve, even more so if the behaviours that may have contributed to that occurrence are still occurring due to illness, due to their ADHD. Although we should seek to rehabilitate, the overriding message throughout this book is that the the book. Each story is being used with the permission of the subject of the study; prevention agenda is and should be at the forefront of our activities. But not only should we seek to prevent problems we should carry out our work in a way that moves the overall agenda forward, seeks to tackle issues from another angle and seeks to stop us getting the same old results from the same old effort. One such way is problem solving.

Case study (1)—Ali's story

All the case studies in this book are true and accurate representations of someone's life that has been affected by ADHD. Each study will in turn be used to amplify the point being made within the surrounding text in at times names have been changed to protect the identity of the individual concerned.

Ali's tale was one of the first stories I heard when I started working with ADHD. As such she retains a place in my emotions that none will shift. I am sure you will agree that her story is both upsetting and uplifting in its own unique way.

Ali was born to a troubled home, her parents argued constantly and eventually the family unit broke up. Ali's mum could not cope with her daughter and Ali was taken into care. As a 'looked after' child in the care of social services she was 'a problem'. She was argumentative, frustrating and difficult to cope with. Ali spent time with different foster carers and always left the fosterers as they could not manage her as she was so 'different'. Ali's school life was disrupted, she lived out of her home area and she developed moods and a very low self-esteem. Over time she became depressed.

School was a place of ridicule and of more disappointment for Ali. Her teachers marginalised her, she was the girl that none of the others would invite to parties and her loneliness grew and grew. Eventually, in the lowest of emotional situations she burned her school down to be rid of it. Not unusually for someone with ADHD she stayed to watch the building burn, as a consequence she was found by the police and arrested.

Psychiatric assessments failed to identify with Ali and she was placed in many forms of treatment programmes. As such her despair grew and grew and her depressive state matured to the point where she was involuntarily taken into a secure psychiatric unit. Her education had ground to a halt, her emotional development was on a negative trajectory and she was becoming a lost cause.

A routine interview with a trained psychiatric social worker, which occurred when Ali was in her late teens, became a watershed point in time. The social worker recognised in Ali the traits of ADHD, a disorder that she had not previously been either diagnosed with or treated for. As she was still 'out of area' the system could not provide psychiatric assessments for her, but her needs continued to expand. Her social worker eventually gained the funding for a private assessment and Ali was diagnosed with ADHD. She was given a care package that included stimulant medication, and in her words her "new life began". Ali went to school, not back to school as in truth she had never really been before. In her first year she gained 'A' levels to sufficiently high standard to be accepted at university, Cambridge University.

Ali maintains a very healthy relationship with her social worker who continues to look after her needs in the most professional manner.

It was the key contact opportunity exploited fully by the social worker that literally changed Ali's life. But how many had been missed along the way, and what if this one had been too?

The purpose of this book is to increase the number of Ali's stories and to reduce the volume of missed key contact opportunities, a simple message in a very complex environment.

Chapter two

Problem solving

POLICING AND problem solving may not grip the reader straight away as being linked, but in the modern day police service there is a tremendous thirst for solving problems rather than merely dealing with policing issues, and there is no valid reason why this philosophy cannot carry over to other services. Perhaps an example may serve as an explanation of how problem solving works.

On summer evenings youngsters gather around a bus shelter in a residential area. Although the kids are not doing anything wrong, the general noise they make, the laughing and their comings and goings do disturb residents nearby who are sat in their front rooms, with windows open, whilst watching the television. This is a common occurrence that most police officers will have dealt with during their years on patrol. The standard response would be to visit the kids, explain the facts, agree that no offences are being caused but that their behaviour is disturbing people and seek the goodwill of the kids to keep the noise down. Perhaps for 24 hours this would be successful, but then the next evening the same problem would arise, maybe a different police officer would attend, but the story would be the same. And so the tale continues, resources tied up, no real effect and a constant situation whereby no one really gets to a successful long-term outcome.

But what if the police officer attending was thinking as a problem solver? Perhaps the bus stop is in the wrong place, shifting it 300 yards down the road to a location outside a factory that is closed in the evening may suit everyone's needs. A quick call to the council and the bus operators, a small one-off investment to move the bus shelter and, hey presto, the residents are happy, the kids are content and the police no longer get the frequent calls to solve the disturbance. This is the essence of problem solving.

Problem solving relies heavily on two models, both having acronyms, SARA and PAT. When deployed together these models provide a different way of thinking that does not just relate to the police, these can be used by any of us to tackle problems differently.

There are some simple dos and don'ts regarding problem solving that are worthy of being repeated at the outset, these are:

> *DO conduct some initial research to find out about the problem and thoughts about the problem in different locations, and their sources.*

DO work out what the overall needs of each problem area are and set a strategy for 'community' involvement accordingly.

DO involve offender and nuisance groups as well as law-abiding citizens where it is important to do so, to address local problems.

DO consider involvement of virtual communities, such as faith groups, ethnic groups, age groups and business groups, as well as geographically defined neighbourhoods.

DO call on local expertise in attempting to tackle complex and difficult problems.

DON'T expect those who are intimidated and fearful to solve their problems on their own from scratch.

DON'T neglect hard to reach or easy to overlook stakeholder groups.

DON'T expect community involvement to let agencies off the hook.

DON'T assume one size fits all for community involvement[1].

SARA

SARA is a four-stage approach to tackling the problem, each of the four elements needs to be considered, and considered in turn.

S Scanning describes the identification of broad issues that need to be addressed
A Analysis describes breaking down problems and their causes
R Response describes what is done to address the problem, in the light of the analysis
A Assessment involves evaluating the effectiveness of what was put in place.

Scanning—What is the problem?

A problem can be anything, including a cluster of similar or recurring incidents, a concern, a place, a person or special event or time. It could also be a combination of these. The first step of the SARA process is to identify the problem in a specific manner. This can be done in many ways, for example:

- Analysis of calls for a particular service
- Incident data analysis—looking specifically for repeat occurrences
- Information and data received via partner agencies
- Community forums
- Analysis of media coverage
- Reviewing public complaints and letters.

---

[1] With acknowledgement of the text in 'Practical lessons for involving the community in crime and disorder problem solving.' Forrest, Myhill and Tilley. (2005).

Analysis—What causes the problem?

Most agencies historically think about problems in terms of the perpetrators involved, almost to the exclusion of other factors. Problem oriented approaches require that a broader range of solutions be explored, which require analysis of the victims and locations of incidents as well as the perpetrator. Comprehensive analysis of problems is critical around all three issues. The first step in analysis is to determine what information is needed. This should be an open, persistent and unbiased process. When analysing problems, certain simple questions should be asked:

- Can we explain the emerging themes?
- Do we know how or why a problem has occurred?
- Do we know of any past attempts to solve it?
- Did those attempts succeed and if not, why not?

PAT

The basic principle of analyzing problems rests on the use of the Problem Analysis Triangle, (PAT). PAT should be used to make the link between three main elements, or causes of any problem. The triangle focuses on the features or characteristics of the **victim**, **perpetrator** or **location,** and the level each plays in creating or sustaining the problem. The model argues that if any of the three issues is effectively taken away, the problem is reduced. Similarly a combination of perpetrators, victims and locations are all contributory factors to problems occurring.

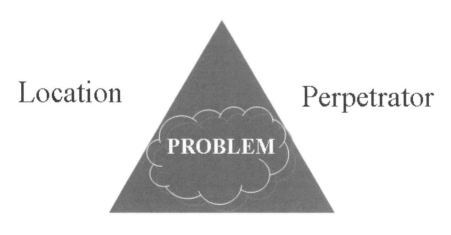

Figure 2

Victim: Recent research has shown that a small number of victims account for a large amount of incidents. In relation to crime, the British Crime Survey found that 4% of the population suffered 44% of all crime. In addition, research in England has shown that victims of burglary, domestic violence and other crimes are likely to be re-victimised, often within a month or two. Effective interventions targeted at repeat victims can have a significant impact on reducing incidents; this is not a phenomenon that relates to just crime.

Perpetrator: In the past much emphasis has been placed on identifying and dealing with perpetrators, often referred to as offenders. Whilst this can some-times reduce a specific problem, the reduction is often temporary as new people come along to replace the original ones. What is required is a fresh approach to the perpetrator side of the triangle. Why are perpetrators attracted to certain victims and places, what do they gain by their behaviour and what could be done to prevent or reduce their rates of causing problems?

Location: Like victims, certain locations account for a significant amount of all criminal activity. Analysis of these locations may indicate why they are so conducive to particular incidents or behaviour and point to ways in which they can be altered. By improving security and design measures, long-term and sustainable solutions can be found. An example of this is the location for services to be delivered, such as an uninviting hospital or the school nurse's office for a meet with a specialist psychiatric nurse.

Responses—What needs to be done?

The third stage of the SARA model focuses on developing and implementing effective responses to the problem—the ultimate challenge. Solutions must be tailored to specific causes. In developing tailored responses, problem solvers should review their findings around the problem analysis triangle. Some, if not most, of the effective responses to problems arise when work-ing in partnership with other agencies. By thinking beyond our normal boundaries and capitalising on what others have to offer, we can signifi-cantly impact on identified issues and problems. There is a requirement for innovative thought and a steer away from the comfort zone of traditional approaches. There are three common key features to all effective responses:

- A response focused on the point at which intervention might be expected to have the longest term and widest impact
- A response which involves some degree of partnership working
- A response which is sustainable, if not necessarily permanent.

Assessment—What has been the impact of the response?

A thorough assessment of the interventions employed must include a belief that a reduction in the issue being considered will not always indicate success. For example, if the parent confidence in the school rises as a result of a problem solving initiative, they may feel more comfortable making complaints; hence a successful outcome might actually be a rise in reported problems. If this was an outcome, both the school and partners must look carefully at the results and assess if these were intended outcomes of the initiative. Assessing the impact of a problem solving effort requires a framework, such as that developed by Eke and Spelman[2], which identifies five different levels or types of positive impact on problems. They are:

- Total elimination of the problem
- Fewer incidents
- Less serious or harmful incidents
- Better handling of the incidents/an improved response to the problem
- Identifying the agency most able to address the problem.

So in a nutshell, that is problem solving. It's a method of working that allows us to think differently and to tackle everyday issues in a different way. Problem solving fits into the world of ADHD in many different ways; how often have we rejected the idea of assisting people whose behaviour doesn't conform? What about dealing with 'problem families' differently by looking to see how we can understand what's going on,and where we have reoccurring issues with a family, who maybe have ADHD, what about learning how we can act differently to bring about positive change to their lives?

Answering those questions, and the many more that arise as a consequence of studying this issue, is the core concept of this book. Throughout the following chapters the responsibility you have as the reader is to ask yourself, 'how does this information assist me to do what I do differently'? By answering that question you should become more effective in your workplace, especially in relation to the 'key contacts' you have with people with ADHD, especially the 'kids of the cone'.

---

[2] Eke and Spelman (2004) in the Practitioners Guide to Problem Solving. Jill Dando Institute. London.

Chapter three

What is ADHD?

T HERE ARE many ways of describing ADHD; the two main descriptions that are reliable are the medically based description and the more straightforward, lay person's way. For completeness I have pulled together these two different descriptions to give the reader every chance of gaining a thorough understanding of this disorder.

An easy way to understand what ADHD is for lay people

ADHD is amongst the most common psychiatric disorders with onset in childhood, although it can, and frequently does persist into adulthood. The brains of people with ADHD function a little differently from those of people without the condition; the areas of the brain affected are those that are responsible for behaviour. The core features of ADHD are therefore behavioural characteristics, specifically:

- Attention difficulties
- Impulsivity
- Hyperactivity.

The way the brain works is extremely complicated, I once witnessed a leading psychiatrist from Boston answering the question 'why is it that the brain is so complicated and difficult to understand?' to which he replied 'if it wasn't we wouldn't be clever enough to actually understand it!' This kind of sums it up really. To put the ADHD difficulties into straightforward language, imagine a car journey from your home to the capital using the motorway system, quite straightforward, a few major roads, a couple of junctions and we know where we are going. Now imagine that same journey without the motorways and major roads, hundreds of little roads, lots of complicated turns and direction changes, but, eventually, we get to the same place. It will have taken longer, been far more arduous and perhaps we may go wrong along the way a few times, but we get there. Well, that's the comparison in thinking patterns for the 'normal' brain, (and I use that word carefully) and the brain for the person with ADHD. It is just difficult to do the same things as everyone else.

The balance of the three symptoms varies from person to person, some children favour hyperactivity, some lean more toward symptoms of attention difficulties. There was a theory that ADHD was mainly found in boys, but recent science suggests that because boys are more likely to be hyperactive they come to our notice more than girls, who drift off in the classroom and don't get 'in the face' of teachers and other adults working with them.

At this point, people new to the ADHD world often state that, 'well I can be a bit hyper at times and often I struggle to concentrate', and that's true for all of us, the difference for ADHD sufferers is that these symptoms are there all of the time, they are pervasive through all of their lives and present in each and every scenario, such as the home, youth clubs and school.

It is worth sticking with those labels for a bit longer though, what does hyperactive mean and how do we recognise inattentive youngsters?

Hyperactivity refers to the inability to sit still, to fidget and to be continually in motion, it may also manifest in incessant noise making and/or talking. Impulsivity appears as difficulty in controlling immediate reactions or inability to think before acting.

To use pictures, people with ADHD have few, if any, 'stop' signs and plenty of 'go' signs in their make-up.

Russ Barkley, one of the world's leading professors on this subject, explains this as an inability to **WAIT, THINK and ACT**.

ADHD is the most common childhood psychiatric disorder and although figures vary from study to study, the generally accepted prevalence figure is that 5% of the population have ADHD.

Now let's transfer those common behaviours into working experiences. Imagine interviewing a young lad who cannot concentrate on your questions, how fair will the interview be? Imagine trying to control a child in a classroom

Figure 3

who bounces around all the time, constantly interrupts and speaks over other schoolmates. And more is the point, no matter how often we ask for things to change, they don't, because these patterns of behaviour aren't chosen by the individual, they happen because of the different brain activities, often called the 'hard wiring'. Once professionals grasp the difference and begin to deploy extra skills into these circumstances things can and will get better, for both the professional and the young person they are dealing with. I refer to this as 'looking behind the behaviour' to see what is the cause. Only then do we as professionals stand any chance of 'solving the problem'.

The medically based way of describing ADHD

Firstly, it is important to confirm that ADHD is a recognised disorder; this is undertaken by referencing Wakefield's standards for a 'valid disorder'[1]. In his work Wakefield describes a valid mental disorder as a 'harmful dysfunction' that comprises a serious deficit or failure in a functional mechanism and it produces harm to the individual in terms of greater mortality, morbidity or impairment in universal major life activities, i.e. cross-cultural activities that must be accomplished at a given age, bonding, self-sufficiency and completed education are good examples. ADHD easily meets both criteria and therefore, whatever the preconceptions, the myths and the false stories permeating the popular media, ADHD is real and is clinically a disorder.

In the Inside story of ADHD,[2] the disorder is explained in terms of brain activity under three main headings, smaller brain structures, under activity in the brain and finally inefficient connections.

Smaller brain structures

In this section of the book references are made to the use of emerging science, such as brain scans that are assisting the medical world to understand ADHD. Research documenting brain differences is beginning to emerge between ADHD individuals and those without the disorder, although as yet, the full significance of these differences is not totally understood. That said, researchers in this field have long posited that a core deficit in frontal lobe function underlies its various cognitive and behavioural manifestations and there is sufficient consistency across studies to make some general conclusions.[3],[4]

The brain has two hemispheres with the right side usually larger than the left. Scientists can now demonstrate through Magnetic Resonance Imaging (MRI)

[1] Wakefield, 1992, 1997
[2] Cape Cod Times, Special Edition, the Inside story of ADHD, June 1998.
[3] Bush, G. (2005), *Functional neuroimaging of ADHD: A review and suggested future directions.* Biol Psychiatry 2005;57:1273-1284
[4] Dickstein, S, Bannon, K, and Castellanos, X et al (2006) *The neural correlates of attention deficit hyperactivity disorder: an ALE meta analysis* Journal; of child psychiatry 47:10 pp 1051–1062

that the right side is an average of 5.2% smaller in individuals with ADHD compared to those that do not have the disorder. The ADHD brain appears to be symmetrical. In particular three separate structures of the brain, the cerebellum, the caudate nucleus and the globus pallidus are smaller in the right side of the brain of people with ADHD.

These are important findings because the cerebellum controls the coordinated expression of movement, the caudate nucleus and globus pallidus translate these commands into action, as such they are responsible for executive functions, such as planning and time management. Therefore the correlation between brain size, especially in key areas and behavioural outcomes, are clearly made.

Under activity in the brain

All brain activity is a process of chemical change, chemicals produce an energy form and this is used by the neuro pathways to stimulate our functionality. People with ADHD have different energy flows in the frontal lobes of the brain, thus, the neuro activity is different to those that do not have the condition. Using Positron Emission Tomography (PET) scans, scientists demonstrate that slower 'sugar' metabolism results in less activity in the areas of the brain linked to attention span and motor control[5], particularly in those diagnosed with ADHD.

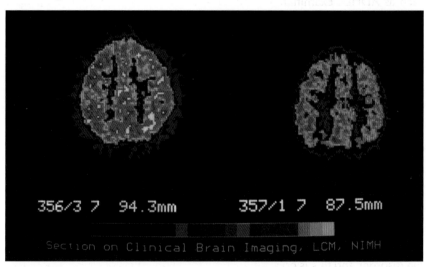

Figure 5[6]

5 New England Journal of Medicine, Vol. 323, pg 1365.
6 Alan Zametkin (1990) Hamburger, S., Cohen, R.M., Brain Metabolism in Hyperactive Adults with Childhood Onset, The New England Journal of Medicine, * 323:1361–1366, 1990. With kind permission

Inefficient connections

Messages move through our brains as a series of electrical impulses, travelling from one nerve ending, across a synapse (a gap), to another nerve ending. Dopamine is the brain chemical, the neurotransmitter that carries the impulses. The more dopamine that is caught as it crosses the synapse, the clearer the message. Although perhaps simplifying the structure of the brain, the following examination does bring to the fore the issues around genetics and synaptic pathways. There are at least five genes responsible for making the elements of the brain that should catch the dopamine, in some brains, those with ADHD, there are deficiencies in two of these. This and defects in the dopamine transporter gene can work together to prevent the structure from efficiently catching sufficient brain chemical from one nerve ending to another. In other words the transmission of the chemical dopamine across the synaptic gap does not occur well enough. This situation can explain lapses in attention, missed information or difficulty in regulating behaviour, and furthermore, if we accept that this not a binary situation of it works or it doesn't, it's progressive along a scale; we can understand how people's behaviour differs.

The use of science explains the deficiencies in the brain and makes the connections between those issues and the behavioural patterns of disorders such as ADHD. Examination of these facts also describes how some people with the disorder can have mild symptoms while others can have strong symptoms, and how the balance between inattention and hyperactivity can vary.

Behavioural inhibition and interference control are crucial to normal functioning; they permit a delay in responding so that thinking can occur, some commentators refer to this as 'Think, Pause, Act'. Expanding this explanation, the effect of this and other characteristics of behaviour, are referred to as a suite of 'executive functions'. These will be examined later, but it is the degradation of these functions that typify the outcomes of ADHD.

Diagnosing ADHD

ADHD is commonly diagnosed through a series of behavioural observations; there is no simple blood test. This gives rise to great debate and some controversy due to a number of contributory factors. There is ongoing discussion and disagreement about the most appropriate diagnostic criteria for the disorder and this is compounded by the fact that two different 'tools' can be used.

In the US there is a bias toward the Diagnostic and Statistical Manual, 4th edition (referred to as DSM IV) and although this is used prolifically in the UK, the official scheme for the NHS is the World Health Organisation's 'International Classification of Mental and Behavioural Disorders, ICD 10'.

The former favours diagnosis of the more inattentive characteristics and the latter the more hyperactive. As Peter Hill and Eric Taylor remark[7] 'the terminology of conditions characterised by over activity, impulsivity, impatience and poorly managed attention is inconsistent'.

The potential for confusion at this point often leads to sceptics having an avenue to dismiss the disorder, as mentioned earlier, often blaming poor parenting. Geoff Kewley[8] asserts that 'society has a deep-rooted belief that poor parenting is responsible for all problem behaviour in children'. But given the heredity nature of ADHD and the issues of coping with the behavioural problems we have discussed, perhaps the reverse is true and family problems can be amplified by the presence of ADHD and the blame culture that seems to exist around 'naughty children'. This brings us back quite sharply to the professional, learning more, getting behind the behaviour and creating an opportunity for themselves to act differently and 'solve the problem'.

As the DSM IV criteria is widely accepted as the leading model for assessing behaviour, it is perhaps worth reviewing what it asks for and in what context, so that the reader is better informed as to the nature of diagnosis.

DSM IV criteria for ADHD (abridged)

- Manifests as six or more symptoms of either inattention or hyperactive-impulsive behaviour
- Symptoms are developmentally inappropriate
- They have existed for at least six months
- They demonstrate cross-setting occurrence, e.g. school, home etc
- They result in impairment in major life activities
- The onset of problems produced impairment by the age of seven
- The symptoms are not best explained by another disorder, e.g. psychosis.

DSM inattention symptoms
- Fails to give close attention to details
- Difficulty in sustaining attention
- Does not seem to listen
- Does not follow through on instructions
- Difficulty in organising tasks or activities
- Avoids tasks requiring sustained mental effort
- Loses things necessary for tasks
- Easily distracted
- Forgetful in daily activities.

Symptoms must occur 'often' or frequently.

---

[7] Hill P & Taylor E (2001) *An audible protocol for treating attention deficit/hyperactivity disorder.* Archives of Disease in Childhood 84:404-409.

[8] Kewley, G (1999) ADHD: recognition, reality and resolution. Learning Assessment Centre Press.

ADHD therefore equals an inability to return to the task when thoughts are disrupted, and there is no evidence that this is selective.

Hyperactive-impulsive symptoms

- Fidgets with hands or feet, or squirms in seat
- Leaves seat in the classroom inappropriately
- Runs about or climbs excessively
- Has difficulty playing quietly
- Is on the go or 'driven by a motor'
- Talks excessively
- Blurts out answers before questions are completed
- Has difficulty in awaiting their turn
- Interrupts or intrudes on others.

Symptoms must occur 'often' or frequently.

The 'core' of the issue is the persistence of inhibition.

Russ Barkley captured all of these symptoms and pulled them together in a comprehensive, yet short statement[9];

> . . . people with ADHD seek immediate reward, rather than growing into delayed gratification, they are poor at problem solving, they struggle to motivate themselves and need external motivation, they are blind to time and they live in the 'now'. People with ADHD need to break the future into smaller pieces, the event, the response and the outcome (ERO), then they can out it all into the 'now'. They do not have a problem knowing what to do; they have a problem doing what they know.

Pure ADHD only truly exists in about one third of sufferers; the remaining two thirds have their ADHD and another 'linked' disorder or condition. These co-occurring conditions are referred to as co-morbidities. It is important that whilst understanding ADHD we understand the conditions that coexist and strive to gather a full picture about the individual we are dealing with.

Comorbid conditions

In a large study carried out in the United States, the Multimodal Treatment Study of Children with ADHD, of the children between the ages of seven to nine years of age diagnosed with ADHD, 70% were found to meet the DSM IV diagnostic criteria for at least one other psychiatric disorder, these included:

---

[9] Barkley, R A (2004) Presentation to the Rome ADHD Conference. November 2004

Oppositional defiant disorder	40%
Anxiety disorder	34%
Conduct disorder	14%
Tic disorder	11%
Depression	4%

Whilst this study only included young children, it does give a picture of the complexity of ADHD and its associated comorbidities. Studies with adults show an even higher incidence of additional disorders accompanying ADHD. Rachel Millstein found that up to 69% of adults with ADHD were diagnosed with a substance abuse problem as well. This particular issue is dealt with in considerable detail in chapter seven. It is noteworthy that the commonly found associated disorders, Oppositional Defiance Disorder (ODD) and Conduct Disorder (CD), are in many cases preventable if the management and treatment of the initial ADHD is satisfactory.

Again, this leads me to comment on the benefits of the prevention agenda and the earliest of professional interventions. In chapter five the statistical significance of conduct disorder in particular is examined, but as a precursor, the costs to the judicial system for a person with pure ADHD were found to be on average roughly £5,000, for those with ADHD and conduct disorder this sum rose to an average of £22,000.

But for now, let's take the opportunity to examine some of the ADHD myths and the responsibility of the media to promote a positive approach to ADHD.

Myths about ADHD

As I discussed earlier a lot of preconceived ideas survive regarding ADHD, if there is one subject that is guaranteed to get a discussion going at a dinner party it is that of 'I work with ADHD'. Some commentators 'know all about it', others 'don't believe it exists' and others 'blame the parents'.

Whilst researching this book I dug around in my files and pulled together a few newspaper headings:

Some headlines question the existence of ADHD . . .

'Do you believe this syndrome really exists? Have your say at . . . asks one popular Sunday newspaper.

'sceptics believe the diagnosis is a 'biobabble' label, which has evolved from a sound bite culture that is too prepared to medicalise antisocial human traits.'

Some question the rights of parents to a second opinion . . .

'Families will go to a doctor and if she or he doesn't believe in ADHD they will find another who will.'

One popular tabloid repeatedly carries negative stories without doing the basic level of homework on the subject . . .

'So have scientists identified an old disease—or invented a new one? The truth is that a disorder or a syndrome is not a medical diagnosis, but a collection of behaviours. These are so broad and vague that almost everyone has them at some point. Getting agitated, losing your temper and being bored are classic symptoms of ADHD—but don't all children behave like that sometimes?'

One article examines the prominent myth that prescription medication leads to addiction . . .

The paper stated that 'fears had been growing about the long-term effects of Ritalin in that it could lead to children being prone to addictions. Dr Kewley stated that "he had been assessing, diagnosing and managing ADHD for many years and had never come across such a case. Indeed, untreated, people with ADHD are predisposed to alcohol and substance abuse, often in an unwitting attempt to self-medicate their condition". In all the patients he sees at his clinic, The Learning Assessment Centre in Horsham, West Sussex, 95% of the children prescribed Ritalin have found it to be of tremendous benefit, whilst only 5% have had some short-term side effects, such as, loss of appetite and sleep problems. He added that he had "never come across a child who had had a craving for his Ritalin"'.

But, there are alternative messages. The media has an important role to play, as do we as professionals, to secure a true understanding of ADHD we should, whenever possible combat, the myths head on. Here are a few of the headlines that have followed my work over the past four years; I include them not to boost my own ego but to encourage all readers of this book that we can make a difference.

'Two Lancashire police officers are establishing a pilot scheme to improve screening for ADHD among young offenders to help reduce juvenile crime. After a recent fact finding trip to the United States, Inspector Phil Anderton told 5Live: 'This condition exists; it's blighting people's lives and disrupting whole families. 'We need to get on top of ADHD. There are also strong links to addiction, particularly drugs and alcohol as a way of self medication'.[10]

'When Phil Anderton, of Lancashire Constabulary's crime prevention unit, made his first visit to Lancaster Farms young offender institution, he was given a guided tour and told it was a 'model prison'. In many ways it was, he says, except in one major respect: common mental disorders were

---

[10] Radio 5 Live interview. 19 November 2004.

23

going unrecognised and untreated. Eighteen months on, there has been a sea change in attitudes, says Anderton. A new screening process is in place, staff are receiving specialist training in attention deficit hyper-activity disorder (ADHD) and a care package is being created to support mentally vulnerable young offenders when they are discharged'.[11]

'Red Arrows host visitors at Blackpool Airport

http://www.deltaweb.co.uk/reds/images/havoc2.jpg *The Team were recently contacted by Lancashire Constabulary, asking if we would host a party of visitors from a local Attention Deficit Hyperactivity Disorder (ADHD) project whilst we were operating from Blackpool Airport.*

Led by Lancashire Constabulary, assisted by a parent support group from Morecambe, the group is run by parents for young people who have Attention Deficit Hyperactivity Disorder (ADHD). The attendees of the group have as a rule been banned from other groups, find it hard to socialise within peer groups and are often marginalised by school, society as a whole and have a low self-esteem. All of this is as a consequence of their ADHD which affects their behaviour. The ground breaking Lancashire project is working with schools, youth workers and the health service to change this[12].

More text regarding the myths about ADHD can be found at appendix 1.

---

[11] The Guardian newspaper. 24 November 2004. Juliet Rix
[12] Red Arrows web site. 15 September 2005.

Chapter four

ADHD and crime

F OR THE most part I am indebted to Professor Russ Barkley for the pro-
vision of the data for ADHD and crime. His longitudinal studies of people
with and without ADHD (his control group) provide the seminal work in this
area. That Professor Barkley has been a good friend to my work in the UK
can only be interpreted as an additional bonus.

Barkley's work is based on science not supposition, which is vital in understanding the strength of this debate. His team analysed many crime types and
ADHD manifestations in terms of behaviour and by building in controls for
conduct disorder (CD) the results allow him to conclude that both ADHD
and CD are a major predictor of crime, especially predatory crime, runaways
and issues around substance abuse (see chapter 7).

Additionally, Geoff Kewley, a UK based neurodevelopmental paediatrician,
has been extremely instrumental in the development of my mindset regarding ADHD and the criminal justice system he states on this subject:

> '*The criminal justice, legal, police system and society in general at the moment,
> appear to have a low awareness that there may well be a genetic or biological
> basis to some criminal activity*'.[1]

I find it hard to disagree with another statement from Geoff that ADHD does
not take away personal responsibilities in relation to crime and criminal
behaviour, but it may at times justify the consideration of mitigating circumstances. **ADHD is not an excuse, it is an explanation.**

Failure to take a wider perspective on crime and its causes enables the high
rate of chronic offending to continue to rise and is cost ineffective. The last
published statistics by the Youth Justice Board confirmed the stark reality that
despite the expensive interventions made over the past five years into the
lives of young criminals', recorded crime committed by young people (U17)
is still rising. Theft, violence, criminal damage, disorder and drug misuse all
continue to show a rising trend.[2]

---

[1] Kewley, G (1999) ADHD: recognition, reality and resolution. Learning Assessment Centre
Press.
[2] Youth Justice Board (2006). Annual Statistics. 2005–6.

Longitudinal studies of criminal behaviour

Barkley's work makes for interesting reading:

- 20% of his control group were arrested.
- 48% of the ADHD group were arrested.

Twice as likely to commit offences.

- The control group were arrested on average 2.1 times.
- The ADHD group were arrested on average 6.4 times.

Three times as many offences.

Immediately we can deduce that having ADHD puts a person at risk of being a prolific offender, but on the positive side, that also indicates that this is predictable and therefore preventable behaviour.

People with ADHD tend to focus on certain types of criminal behaviour; these can easily be pulled together into three main headings:

- Predatory crimes, muggings, fighting and weapon use
- Self-sufficiency crimes such as stealing, running away from care, prostitution
- Drug related crimes, including possession, supplying and stealing to provide for a habit.

The following table outlines the particular crime types that participants in Barkley's studies reported that they themselves admitted undertaking:

	Control group	ADHD group
Stealing	36%	50%
Being disorderly	53%	69%
Assaults with a weapon	7%	22%
Burglary	8%	20%
Arson	6%	15%
Running away from home	16%	31%

All together there appears a compulsive argument regarding the risks of entering the criminal justice system for people with ADHD, this being reinforced by both findings from longitudinal studies and from self-reporting of lifetime occurrences. There is perhaps one last category of risk that is worth exploring in this discussion, that of being ultimately more vulnerable.

Vulnerability and increased risk

I first encountered this element of risk for people with ADHD in conversation with a parent whose son had just been sent to prison for robbery. The conversation was unusual for a number of reasons, firstly, the parent was engaging a 'cop' in a meaningful conversation without fear of prejudice or being seen to be trying to interfere with her son's trial, and secondly, because both parties, and I include myself, were able to discuss the issues in an 'adult' and forthright manner, with learning taking place on both sides. The pattern of behaviour has been reinforced in many such conversations with parents, across Europe and the United States. There is a common denominator, children, and especially boys, with poorly managed or treated ADHD are particularly easily led, and in so being they are often 'left out in the cold' when law enforcement agencies arrive at the scene of a crime.

To expose this risk we have to track back a little in the young person's life, this pathology is examined in greater detail in chapter eight. Having been pushed aside in school, forced out of the 'normal' peer group and suffering from a recognisable low self-esteem, many young boys and girls seek solace in the company of older lads. Finding himself 'adopted' by such groups or gangs the young lad with ADHD falsely believes he is being accepted, perhaps for the first time. Often, if not frequently, the gangs of lads are, quite simply, troublemakers and they seek to use the impressionable and vulnerable lad with ADHD, who begins to cling onto them, as a 'gofer', an errand boy. But on many occasions the errands become unlawful, the 'dares' become riskier, and the patterns of behaviour escalate rapidly.

Compliance with the tasks, dares or errands, equates to acceptance for the new group member and options such as saying 'no', and withdrawal are not considered, even on the advice or insistence of parents and carers. Grounding the boy leads to late night adventures commencing with climbing out of bedroom windows, escalating to not coming home, to running away, to becoming a runaway. When the venture goes wrong, the crime being committed is discovered, the young lad with ADHD looks over his shoulder to find he is on his own, caught, arrested and in his parents eyes, in trouble. Of course, in the eyes of the newly adopted peer group this is the action of a 'hero', acceptance is seen as greater and no matter what warnings are given, the chances of standard preventative measures being affective are continually minimised.

On too many occasions I have spent time with parents who are somewhere on this trajectory with their son. On one occasion, this led to stealing car keys from Mum's handbag, as a dare by his mates, on another, stealing a credit card, another smoking of cannabis as a group, at home whilst Mum was at work. The obvious encouragement to skip school is a further example of this behaviour.

Standard justice based interventions have not worked in many of the cases I have examined. To link back to Barkley's work discussed earlier, it's of little use for officers of agencies and parents telling the lads in question that they shouldn't be doing these things, they know that, the difficulty is for them doing what they know to be right, especially in the circumstances of low self-esteem, and there being, for them, apparently no alternative peer group or options. Again, it is incumbent on all the professionals with key contact opportunities to identify with this pattern of behaviour, to get behind the behaviour that is presented and to solve the problem through a different approach, one that is bespoke and specific to the unique circumstances of ADHD.

One parent with whom I spent considerable time was literally at her wits end, and was identifying that she was right at the crisis point in her son's offending behaviour, and she was at a loss as to what to do. She had, in her mind, tried everything, ranging from spoiling her son with gifts through to strong arm tactics with grounding and withdrawal of any 'privileges' when behaviour was unacceptable.

Coping strategies for potential young offenders

Pulling ideas and strategies together to assist parents in these circumstances has proven to be, for me in my work, one of the elements of advice that at least gives parents some hope. I would not claim to be a behaviour expert in this field, but for completeness I include in this chapter a short list of ideas that professionals I have worked with and listened to, have recommended:

- Top of the list, exercise and lots of it. There is no equal to hard, physical exercise for youngsters with ADHD, it assists the chemical flow in the brain, overcomes the pent up energy issues and has a profound effect on motivation.
- Choose exercise programmes carefully, the idea of playing baseball, where the youngster has to wait in line for their go, and then has a go, fails to get the eye and hand coordination right and makes a fool of themselves, leads more often than not into a situation where the body of another team member gets struck with the bat rather than the ball.
- Boxing, a punch bag in the garage works well. Running, perhaps with a partner, is an excellent and reasonably cheap sport that works well. I have worked with and witnessed parents who manage their child's behaviour solely by the use of hard, punishing, road running, it is especially successful when the runs are an inclusive activity and have a positive motivational element.
- Team sports need special handling, particularly if team members have little chance of understanding the particular needs of the participant with ADHD. The increased likelihood of wanting to always be in the thick of the action, not liking being 'off the ball', being outspoken in briefings and rule setting meetings can all lead to exclusion, which clearly defeats the objective.

- Motivation through reward is frequently proven to have an effect. The parent or carer has to be consistent in their approach, fair with sanctions and rewards, and constantly on top of their game to keep the scenario motivating and challenging.
- Finally, find out what the young person with ADHD is actually good at, wants to do and let them do it. There are many true anecdotes of kids being held responsible for pet care at school, running school magazines, taking up a musical instrument within reason it matters not what it is. Importantly, the parent / carer may have to be extremely creative to find the relevant niche, but once found, given a positive reward mechanism, the results have frequently been outstanding.

Given the level of funding for Positive Activities for Young People (PAYP) and other Youth Justice based preventative programmes, the invitation for professionals in this field is clear, identify the potential children that require individual care and attention, spend time with them, their parents and teachers, find out what will make them motivated, and invest in that. The false expectation that young teenage children with ADHD will enjoy summer schemes based around basket weaving[3] may not always deliver the expected outcome.

---

[3] Witnessed by the author in one summer scheme for potential offenders.

Chapter five

ADHD and crime—the statistics

YOUNG PEOPLE with ADHD are at increased risk of academic failure, dropping out of school or college, teenage pregnancy and criminal behaviour, of that there is clarity. When my research commenced the simple question that was posed was, 'does having ADHD make you a criminal?' There can be only one answer to that question, 'NO!' But, having ADHD does increase the risk, as we have explored, of young people becoming criminalised and entering the justice system.

There is a natural tendency for researchers in the UK to stay with either English research (of which there is little) or American findings, of which there are a lot, due to the language barriers posed, especially by European work. But, having quoted Barkley's findings in this book, it is perhaps prudent to stray into some European research findings to assist in understanding the scale of the ADHD and crime issue. For some readers, European research provides a piece of mind that cannot be satisfied through American literature, no matter how significant the findings are.

In 2002 Kirsten Rasmussen and colleagues[1] in Norway evaluated male prisoners convicted of murder, other violent acts, sexual offences, arson, fraud, theft, drug- or alcohol-related crimes, or serious traffic crimes. Using a range of tests, the researchers calculated the rates of past childhood ADHD, among the subjects. They found that:

- 46 percent of the prisoners exceeded the cut-off score of 46 for ADHD on the Wender Utah Rating Scale, and another 18 per cent scored in the screening window of 35 to 45
- 30 per cent of the prisoners met criteria for adult ADHD, and an additional 16 percent had scores indicating probable ADHD
- 86 per cent of the prisoners qualified for a diagnosis of personality disorder, with a significant relationship seen between ADHD and personality disorders.

In summary, the researchers say their data indicate that "persistent ADHD, comorbid with both personality disorders and reading disability, constitutes a problem of great magnitude among prisoners".

---

[1] "Attention deficit hyperactivity disorder, reading disability, and personality disorders in a prison population", Kirsten Rasmussen, Roger Almvik, and Sten Levander, *Journal of the American Academy of Psychiatry and the Law, Vol. 29,* 2001, 186–93.

5% v 46%

Let's put those findings into perspective. Given the acknowledged 5% prevalence figure in the general population, the disproportionate prevalence in the prison population is startling.

Closer to home in the UK, in her book 'ADHD in adults'[2], Susan Young intimates that she found that up to 25% of the British prison population had ADHD as children.

In 1997 her Majesty's Inspector of Prisons[3] conducted research into the UK's prison population. They found that 'the recent study of the health of prisoners aged 16–24 revealed that mental health problems were very common; 23% had discussed emotional problems with their doctor. Research has shown that mental health and emotional difficulties are major problems for young people in prison; over 50% of remanded young males and over 30% of sentenced young males have a diagnosable mental disorder'.

The UK Office for National Statistics found in 2000[4] that the general population had a 1 in 10 prevalence of mental health disorders, whereas 4 out of 10 sentenced young men and 2 out of 3 young women aged 16 to 20 had mental health issues.

Pratt[5] in 2002 found a statistically significant overall effect of ADHD on crime and delinquency. In his list of recommendations he suggests there is growing evidence of a high prevalence rate of ADHD among prison inmates and it seems likely that this condition is impairing the ability of offenders to cope effectively with the strains and demands of imprisonment. Offenders with ADHD, he suggests, can be expected to be challenged by impulsivity in an environment that expects conformity, demands from correctional officers to attend to instructions and 'follow orders', and tasks that require lengthy attentiveness (e.g. classroom instruction, job assignments).

In 1996 Farrington made the following observations in his respected book entitled 'Understanding and Preventing Youth Crime':

> "Hyperactivity and impulsivity are among the most important personality or individual-difference factors that predict later delinquency."

I could go on and on, and for the reader that has a more than passing interest in the statistics I would strongly recommend the use of Crime Times on the autism website http://www.autismwebsite.com/crimetimes/subjects.htm and reference to the work of Russ Barkley http://www.autismwebsite.com/crimetimes/subjects.htm

---

[2] Susan Young et al (2006) ADHD in Adults: A Psychological Guide to Practice Wiley.
[3] HMIP (1997) Young Prisoners HMSO.
[4] National Office for Statistics (2000) Psychiatric morbidity in young offenders. HMSO.
[5] Travis C Pratt, et al (2002) Department of Political Science/Criminal Justice, Washington State University,

Chapter six

ADHD and outcomes

WHEN MY work with ADHD commenced, it had an initial focus on crime reduction, but as time moved on the activities very soon began to take on a more social outcome based approach, looking for better outcomes for young people. The overall goal to this day is to promote within professionals a wider knowledge base, and a problem solving philosophy aimed at allowing young people with ADHD more chances of achieving their birth potential, as explored and highlighted in the 'kids of the cone' model.

Motivation comes in many forms, but my experience whilst working with the many agencies that can deal with ADHD has demonstrated that one way of bringing about change is to demonstrate some of the potential negative outcomes that may manifest if that change doesn't come about. This chapter outlines research findings that demonstrate that without any doubt, people who have poorly managed ADHD suffer, and they suffer in terms of reduced opportunities in adult life.

Outcomes in adult life

Weiss[1] is one of many researchers who have proven that as many as 60% of individuals with ADHD symptoms in childhood continue to experience difficulties in adult life. Adults with ADHD are more likely to be dismissed from employment and have tried a multitude of jobs before they have been able to find the one that is the 'square peg in the square hole', the right one for them. Researchers, backed up by my own findings, frequently discover that adults with ADHD who do find work have a predisposition to self-employed activities.

As well as the interpersonal difficulties discussed throughout this book, lateness, absenteeism, errors of judgment and an inability to complete complex tasks all play their part in the negative employment spiral for adults with ADHD.

But perhaps the oasis in the desert can materialise, especially when the management of ADHD is in a more effective form. I recently worked with a

---

[1] Weiss, G (1985) Psychiatric status of hyperactives as adults. Journal of American Psychiatry 1985.

senior police officer who undoubtedly had ADHD tendencies, but like many adults he had no formal diagnosis, his son did, but he didn't. His conduct in meetings was at times difficult, he was frequently outspoken and this was often to the detriment of his peer group. But when this man found out that I worked in the field of ADHD he was able to discuss his issues more openly, he found understanding and we were able to work together with a plan to increase his effectiveness and reduce his rejection by his fellow team members. That says more about him than me, but amplifies that an understanding of ADHD can and does provide better workplace outcomes.

In 2006 Joe Biederman published research that confirmed that significantly more adults with ADHD had deficits of executive functioning than comparison subjects. Deficits of executive functioning were associated with lower academic achievement, irrespective of ADHD status. Subjects with ADHD deficits of executive functioning had a significantly lower socio-economic status and a significant functional morbidity beyond the diagnosis of ADHD alone. Biederman's findings concentrate and define outcomes using the executive functioning model, and for a more detailed analysis of this I refer to the work of Tom Brown who concludes that 'attention is essentially a name for the integrated operation of the executive functions of the brain'.

Executive functions

Brown describes the clusters of functions in the brain as an orchestra. In a well schooled, well managed orchestral situation, with a competent conductor, the sound of music is sweet, predictably of quality and a joy to behold. For each instrument read a function of the brain, for the conductor read the control mechanisms of the brains command centre, located in the pre-frontal cerebral cortex, one of the main areas of the brain affected by ADHD. When ADHD is present, the conductor doesn't function, the instruments in the orchestra play out of tune and out of synch with each other and the net result is a cacophony that can be rather unpleasant to behold. The relationships between behavioural clusters fail to work continuously with others and the executive functioning of the individual under examination reveals deficits.

In his book 'Attention Deficit Disorder, The Unfocused mind in Children and Adults', Brown[2] breaks down executive functioning into six key areas that, ordinarily, should work together. A concise review of these functional areas leads the reader into understanding how ADHD relates to outcomes in life.

1 Organising, prioritising and activating work

Difficulties in starting tasks, particularly those that are not interesting, is a

---

[2] Brown, T (2005) *'The unfocused mind in children and adults'* Yale University Press.

problem for people with ADHD. Tasks are put to one side until the demand is at crisis point. Procrastination often leads to an increased risk of, if not the eventuality, of being fired. People with ADHD have an innate inability to judge how much work they can achieve and often over promise and under deliver on their activities. In a presentation to an ADHD based conference, a leading television producer, who has ADHD, admitted that he had trouble saying no, didn't manage his diary effectively and as a consequence, shamefully struggled to deliver to his agreed schedules.

2 Focusing, sustaining and shifting attention to tasks

Focusing on a task is difficult for people with ADHD, as is sustaining that focus for as long as is normally required. Barkley describes the issue as not one of being able to focus, rather one of being able to maintain a focus on the matter in hand when all around there are distractions that can, and will, take the focus off the primary goal. Imagine an auto-focus camera that has zoomed in on the subject to be photographed, a small bird for instance. As the shutter release is pressed the camera hunts around, focusing on a host of other things in the viewfinder, steadfastly refusing to return the focus to the bird. When the focus does return, the bird has flown, in real terms; the opportunity to complete the task has been lost. This isn't a situation that is unique to people with ADHD, but persons with ADHD report that this is a minute by minute occurrence rather than the occasional happening.

3 Regulating alertness, sustaining effort and processing speed

For many with ADHD, being required to sit still and be quiet leads to drowsiness, for some they report being borderline narcoleptic. This is an issue that frequently manifests when trying to read. The best example is to liken this to the feeling we have when lying in bed at the end of a long, tiring day. Reading the novel of choice we suddenly realise that we have read the last few paragraphs a number of times, and still have no recollection of the content. The hint for us is that it is time for sleep. But if this is a common occurrence all day, every day, the situation is different. People with ADHD also report running out of steam when the task is of no or little interest to them, especially when there is little immediate reward. Barkley believes that people with ADHD need immediate reward and cannot wait for a delayed gratification, the workplace rarely provides this form of extrinsic payback in real time. Rob Doyle highlights this issue in a vignette about a man with ADHD trying to complete a complicated thesis.

'I just cannot get down to writing this piece.'
'Are you motivated enough to complete the work?'
'I do want to, but it's boring and tedious.'
Sensing motivation was the key, the doctor changed tack. . . .
'If I promised to pay you one million dollars upon completion, which I will, could you do it?'

'Of course I could.'

And he did, although I doubt the million was handed over, the core issue was motivation and the ability to overcome the profound difficulties of having ADHD and the connection to motivation.

4 Managing frustration and modulating emotions

The executive functioning model steps out of the criteria for ADHD diagnosis at this juncture, DSM IV does not include any items referring to emotions. Yet, commonly, clinicians report that patients with ADHD frequently, if not constantly, struggle to manage their emotions. It has been my experience with the adults with ADHD I work with, that emotional outbursts are difficult to predict and hard for the lay person to empathise with. I recall being at a conference on adult ADHD and sitting in the dining hall with a colleague and a lady with diagnosed ADHD. It was approaching the time for the afternoon tea break and we anticipated all the delegates descending into the hall for refreshments. Although we had noticed that the drinks and biscuits were not yet ready, my colleague and I could pass this off with a mere shrug, but for the lady with ADHD this was a significant issue. It was important enough for her to leave our discussion, find a member of staff to 'rant' to about sloppy standards and demand things were put right immediately. This lady had no responsibility for the conference at all, but the issue quickly became one of great importance to her.

People with ADHD report having short fuses, and a low threshold for irritability. This makes for very complex workplace interactions, especially if the background to this behaviour is not understood by colleagues and employers.

5 Utilising working memory and assessing recall

Most people with ADHD complain of difficulties holding onto one train of thought, especially when being asked to multi-task and also consider something else. These difficulties are referred to as being in the 'working memory' rather than the long-term memory. The working memory is unrelated to the 'short-term memory'; it's the equivalent of RAM on a computer which processes the items being stored in the background. Working memory has many functions, such as holding onto a piece of information whist attention is temporarily diverted onto another task. It's as if there isn't a 'hold' button on the memory.

Working memory is essential says Brown for participation in group discussions, or complex discussions where one is required to listen and understand the words of a participant in the conversation whilst formulating their own response to be delivered at the appropriate moment.

Miyake and Shah[3] describe that working memory plays an important part in moment by moment integration of the memories internally held in long-term storage and those transient memories coming in real time from external sources.

Working memory is complex, but what is straightforward is that chronic impairments in this system are an important aspect of ADHD.

6 Monitoring and self-regulating action

The wild, reckless children that are 'out of control' typify most peoples appreciation of ADHD, this being the interpretation of hyperactivity and behaviour that is impulsive. It is this aspect of ADHD that rises to the behavioural surface mostly due to the highly visible nature of these behavioural traits. Barkley argues that impaired abilities to inhibit behaviour is the primary problem of ADHD and of all the executive functioning it is this that has the greater affect on social outcomes. Tom Brown argues that there is an additional element to this however, and that is in terms of being able to 'stop' when required; people with ADHD cannot always proceed to 'go' in an appropriate manner. His example of the difficulties in crossing the street safely highlights this issue. Whereas it is vital that the ability to stop prevents a road user from dangerously running straight out into the path of oncoming traffic, the ability to assimilate all the information around the individual so they can cross safely, such as the traffic flow, the speed and direction of traffic and the proximity of the next place of safety, is also important. A deficit at this point in time may well lead to dire consequences.

In chapter 8 we explore the relationship between driving and ADHD in greater detail, but as one of the primary causes of death and injury in the UK, we cannot for one minute focus on social outcomes without more than a passing review of the links between ADHD and the complex pastime of using the roads. Crossing the street is a good example to continue with, especially as the research is clear that road users, particularly child pedestrians with ADHD, are at an increased risk of injury and this is a factor that is often overlooked.

Brown states that there are four coordinated functions that should occur to do almost anything carefully; they are especially prevalent in the actions of a road user:

1 Inhibiting the action until the right moment

---

[3] Miyake, A and Shah, P (1999) Models of working memory: mechanisms of active maintenance and executive control. New York. Cambridge University Press.

2 Monitoring one's self and the specific circumstances of the situation to decide how and when to act
3 Executing the appropriate actions when needed
4 Monitoring one's self and the current situation while acting.

To carry out these functions both sequentially and also in parallel presents any person with challenges, but for the person with ADHD it is clear that these requirements lead to increased chances of failure, which can be damaging both mentally and physically.

Another key aspect of the executive function of regulating behaviour emerged very quickly in my studies of ADHD and the criminal justice system. For many reasons, police officers, nurses, teachers etc, are all very professionally aware of the importance of personal space. Many are taught not to invade others 'space' when teaching, advising a motorist, or just in conversation. For some the training continues into recognising the dangers that could be about to surface when someone invades your personal space, such as a patrolling police officer quickly assessing threatening behaviour being exuded by someone on the streets.

An important aspect of self-monitoring for people with ADHD is the lack of ability to self-monitor and to monitor context during conversations. Brown's four point list above highlights that there is a difficulty in being attentive to facial expressions, tone of voice, subtle eye movement that signals impatience, falling interest or increased tension. People with ADHD report having incredible difficulty reading other people's body language and frequently the personal space of others is invaded, and social detachment from a conversation does not occur in a timely fashion. For professionals working with people with ADHD this is an extremely important issue that requires full understanding. Confrontation in conversation is almost guaranteed, people getting 'in your face' is almost a certainty and it is a given that short, snappy conversations will not occur as detachment and pulling away is rare to the extreme.

It could be said that to appreciate these issues we are guilty of stereotyping, but, given that most people see stereotyping as a negative, there are many instances where such an understanding allows greater insight, and I would argue strongly that this is one of those occasions.

To conclude this chapter I refer back to my experiences as a police trainer where we would use the conscious competence model[4] to explain how we sometimes have emotional difficulty when we are learning and how when

---

[4] W C Howell and E A Fleishman (eds.), Human Performance and Productivity. Vol. 2: Information Processing and Decision Making. Hillsdale, NJ: Erlbaum; 1982.

we understand that we learn in stages, we can assist others to deal with feelings more effectively. This model amplifies a traditional subconscious process that we all follow when dealing with other people in professional scenarios, it is my submission that as you read this text you will appreciate that instead of following the 'normal' flow from stage 1 through to stage 4, for the person with ADHD there is a great difficulty in getting past stage 1, and the responsibility on us as professionals is to accept this and solve the 'problem' differently.

In terms of behaviour and the use of social interaction, the main responsibility falls on us as professionals to understand and get behind the behaviour to increase the positive opportunities arising from each and every interaction we have.

Stage 1 of learning

Unconscious incompetence

- The person is not aware of the existence or relevance of the skill area
- The person is not aware that they have a particular deficiency in the area concerned
- The person might deny the relevance or usefulness of the new skill
- The person must become conscious of their incompetence before development of the new skill or learning can begin
- The aim of the trainee or learner, and the trainer or teacher, is to move the person into the 'conscious competence' stage, by demonstrating the skill or ability and the benefit that it will bring to the person's effectiveness. *There is an anticipated struggle at this stage of normalised processes, because of the inability to do what they know is right by people with ADHD.*

Stage 2

Conscious incompetence

- The person becomes aware of the existence and relevance of the skill
- The person is therefore also aware of their deficiency in this area, usually by attempting or trying to use the skill
- The person realises that by improving their skill or ability in this area their effectiveness will improve
- Ideally the person has a measure of the extent of their deficiency in the relevant skill, and a measure of what level of skill is required for their own competence
- The person ideally makes a commitment to learn and practice the new skill, and to move to the 'conscious competence' stage. *Again, the difficulties arise with doing what is known to be right, and any coach or professional who has an expectation that the learner will change or seek to develop as a consequence of feedback in these circumstances,*

needs to address the issue for people with ADHD with a different mindset.

Stage 3

Conscious competence

- The person achieves 'conscious competence' in a skill when they can perform it reliably at will
- The person will need to concentrate and think in order to perform the skill
- The person can perform the skill without assistance
- The person will not reliably perform the skill unless thinking about it—the skill is not yet 'second nature' or 'automatic'
- The person should be able to demonstrate the skill to another, but is unlikely to be able to teach it well to another person
- The person should ideally continue to practise the new skill, and if appropriate commit to becoming 'unconsciously competent' at the new skill
- **Practise** is the single most effective way to move from stage 3 to stage 4. *For the person with ADHD, there may well be a temporary demonstration of the new skill, but we should expect an almost complete and immediate remission due to the difficulties we have analysed with behaviour, the question, 'you have been told not to do that, why did you do it again?' is a breath wasting expose on behalf of the questioner that they have little or no comprehension of the behavioural difficulties for a person with ADHD. Patterns of behaviour that do not meet the 'normal' expectations of society will be repeated by people with ADHD, even after they have been coached to do so differently, not through choice, but because they are not in full control. They are, and for most if not all will remain, hard wired differently. **This is not a debate about will power; it's a debate about ability to perform due to a disorder.***

Stage 4

Unconscious competence

- The skill becomes so practised that it enters the unconscious parts of the brain—it becomes 'second nature'
- Common examples are driving, sports activities, typing, manual dexterity tasks, listening and communicating
- It becomes possible for certain skills to be performed while doing something else, for example knitting while reading a book
- The person might now be able to teach others in the skill concerned, although after some time of being unconsciously competent the person might actually have difficulty in explaining exactly how they do it—the skill has become largely instinctual
- This arguably gives rise to the need for long-standing unconscious competence to be checked periodically against new standards. *The results*

expressed in stage 4 of the model present great difficulties for the person with ADHD. I have included this stage deliberately as it exposes our expectations, and in the circumstances of the professional seeking to do a better job, it is our responsibility to adjust our expectations to a level of understanding that will maintain our motivation to continue to bring about positive outcomes.

This model dovetails neatly into the world of ADHD. Whereas the average learner has the ability to reflect and assist themselves through the stages, there is a responsibility on us as professionals to tackle our key contact opportunities differently. When we appreciate that identifying that they are unconsciously incompetent, is almost impossible for some especially in relation to the regulatory aspects of executive functioning, (and I refer of course to those people with ADHD,) we will begin to problem solve.

Progressive behavioural patterns

Many people rely on Geoff Kewley's model of the stages of ADHD, it is often adapted, as I will do here, but the core context remains the same. The underlying message is that the one third of people with pure ADHD, the progression toward other issues is predictable to a degree, and therefore, I would argue manageable. If this trajectory is manageable, it may well be preventable.

In terms of outcomes for people with ADHD, the most frighteningly pre-

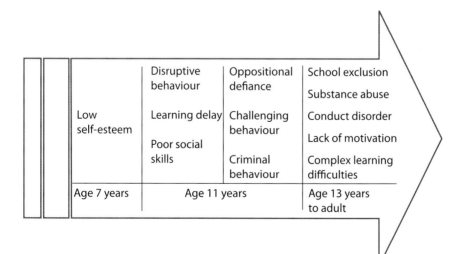

Figure 7

dictable result of poorly understood and poorly managed ADHD is the prospect of migrating to the comorbid position of having ADHD and conduct disorder. It is frightening mainly due to the incredibly heightened risk of moving into problematic drug use, the subject of the next chapter of this book. There are a wide range of life patterns for people with ADHD, not all will demonstrate a conduct disordered lifestyle and abuse of drugs, but there are a significant number and that in itself is an underestimated outcome of ADHD.

Chapter seven

ADHD and problematic drug use

F OR THE past two years I have been indebted to an academic colleague, Alastair Roy, who has worked alongside me in the push to alter the process of drug treatment for people with ADHD in the UK. In this chapter I will unashamedly fall back on our mutual work that will take the reader on a unique journey through the statistics on the subject. This culminates in an examination of the need for an alternative method of assisting troubled ADHD based users of drugs, who undoubtedly have problems as a consequence of the lack of understanding of these important and unique issues.

There is a valid question of 'why is using substances a problem?' There are many myths about drug use and drug users. The most popular would appear to be that any illicit drug use leads to addiction and thus to a loss of control and a decline into crime. Drugs research has played its part in the continuance of the myths, as nearly all funded research leads to the messages that 'drugs are bad, and all people that 'do' drugs are bad people'. The current agenda therefore fails to differentiate between those users that experience problems and those that do not. The widespread failure to understand some of the real issues behind **problematic drug use** is damaging and missing the point.

The UK and the USA have for a considerable period of time been engaged in a war on drugs, yet there is no realisation that all wars have casualties and this 'war' leaves a trail of unwanted social effects. Perhaps the use of the expression 'war' is misplaced?

The vast majority of people that use drugs do so with few consequences, these are often known as 'recreational users'. As lifestyle changes occur with maturity, most stop using illicit drugs in response to their work and family life demands. Furthermore, most people consume alcohol throughout their adult life and for the vast majority this is not a problem but a social lubricant.

This all culminates in true expressions of lifestyle, that 'drugs can be fun, drink can be fun, so what is the problem?'

The answer to that question lies in the fact that for some, a significant minority, the use of substances such as alcohol and illicit drugs does cause problems and is not something that can be stopped at a moment's notice. As a consequence this can disrupt one's motivation and ability to pursue education, to work, to interact with others or to maintain a household.

Whilst many authors 'prove the point' that having ADHD puts a person at a greater risk of having problematic drug use issues, few pin down the reasoning for this. There is one overriding theory that forms the mainstream of opinion, that of self-medication. In this book we examine this theory through case studies and anecdotal evidence and go on to formulate the emerging observation that in the life of a person with ADHD there are 'tipping points', where if the right interventions do not come into their lives, in the right way, they could easily tip over into a lifestyle that brings substance use into their lives at a time of crisis. It's often a case of wrong place, wrong time, no understanding or help.

In the UK the Home Office estimates that 3% of drug users are problematic users. There are few studies in the UK that link the prevalence of ADHD and problematic drug use, but other studies draw conclusions that problematic drug users differ from other drug users and often have one or more vulnerabilities; social exclusion, poverty, abuse, lived in the care system or been a runaway from care. In my professional experience I draw from anecdotal conclusions that these catchment groups contain a high, a disproportionately high, number of people with behavioural disorders such as ADHD.

As we examined earlier, ADHD is a highly comorbid disorder; McGough,[1] in 2005, found that 87% of people suffering from ADHD had at least one and 56% had at least two other psychiatric disorders, compared with 64% and 27% respectively, in non-ADHD subjects. ADHD was associated with greater disruptive behaviour, substance use, mood and anxiety disorders and with

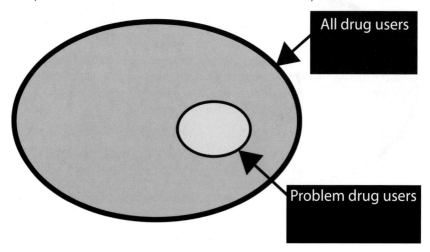

All drug users

Problem drug users

Figure 8

---

[1] James J McGough (2005) Psychiatric Comorbidity in Adult Attention Deficit Hyperactivity Disorder: Findings from Multiplex Families.

earlier onset of major depression, oppositional defiant disorder, and conduct disorder. Molina and Pelham[2] in 2003 had reported that their research found that among subjects with ADHD, the persistence of ADHD and adolescent conduct disorder were each associated with elevated substance use.

The situation is more acute than people with ADHD merely having a higher than average propensity to misuse drugs. Among those diagnosed with ADHD, Wilens[3] found a heightened risk of developing drug use problems, an acceleration of the transition from less severe drugs or alcohol abuse to more severe dependence, and a doubling of the duration of substance misuse before remission.

There is also an overlap between problematic drug use and families with ADHD, this may be genetic but it could also be environmental. Probably it is a combination of the two, with differing relationships for different circumstances.

More ADHD symptoms = more drug use

More serious drug use = more ADHD symptoms in patient history[4]

As a consequence of this research we can categorically state that the relationship between ADHD and problematic drug is real, and needs to be understood. At the minimum, this relationship redraws the diagram of concentric circles to form a different, and worrying, new shape.

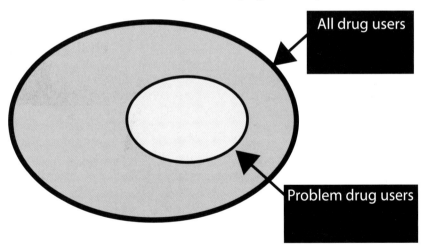

Figure 9

---

[2] Molina B S and Pelham W E Jr. (2003) *Childhood predictors of adolescent substance use in a longitudinal study of children with ADHD. J Abnorm Psychology.*

[3] Wilens, T (2000) Attention deficit hyperactivity disorder across the lifespan. Annual review of Medicine 53.

[4] Biederman, J (1995) American Journal of Psychiatry.

There are three models offered as explanation of this relationship, the Stepping Stone model, the Risk Factor model and the sub-type model.

Relationship models for ADHD and problematic substance use

The **Stepping Stone** model suggests that the presence of ADHD may be a step on the pathway to problems with drugs, which requires the development of conduct disorder (CD) or oppositional defiance disorder (ODD) to bring about the drugs problems. As we discussed earlier, the onset of conduct disorder and ODD can be prevented if the professionals make the right interventions into someone's life at the right time the key contact opportunities message again.

For professionals this makes the requirement for them to know and understand the people with ADHD in their charge, and to look for the 'tipping points' (identified by the mark TP in the following diagrams). In so doing this process gives them the opportunity to intervene correctly and then possibly, if not probably, fend off a negative outcome from the contact made at this key time.

$$\textbf{ADHD} \longrightarrow \textbf{ODD/CD} \longrightarrow \textbf{Drug use}$$
$$\textbf{TP}$$

Figure 10

The **Risk Factor** model looks at the outcome from a different angle, in doing so it incorporates other factors that may have a consequence on the outcome of a person's life due to the presence of ADHD.

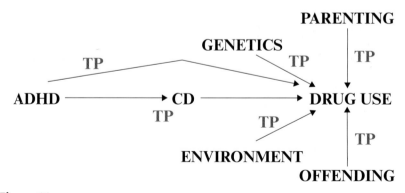

Figure 11

The suggestion is consistent with the high levels of overlap between substance misuse and conduct disorder, and also with the claimed reality that CD is just one of many risk factors for problematic drug use. The model demonstrates the complex issues for professionals, as tipping points can and most probably will be found in relation to any of the environmental factors that prevail in the young person's life. To complicate matters, most of the factors highlighted are dealt with by separate agencies, and therefore the responsibility to share information on a young person when a tipping point is anticipated is vital for successful management of the problem.

The **Sub Type** model offers that individuals with coexisting ADHD and CD may represent a unique diagnostic subgroup best described as some form of fledgling psychopathy. This model suggests that, in relation to the risks for problematic drug use, the risk is different from 'pure' ADHD to that of ADHD combined with conduct disorder.

The model is very consistent with research findings that suggest that this group of young people, those with co-morbid ADHD and CD, have poorer outcomes in a number of areas of life including higher levels of, and more persistent anti-social behaviour, including offending. In 2003 Flory and Lynham suggested that "there is a need for researchers to examine the relationship between different sub-types of ADHD and CD and substance use

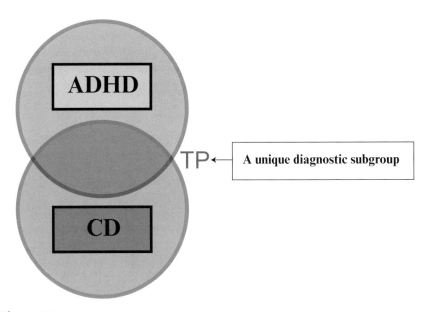

Figure 12

outcomes"[5]. The overriding point to emerge from this model is that the progression from the purist ADHD toward clinical conduct disorder can be observed and tackled. Should it not be, or if the young person concerned has previously slipped through the net and the ADHD/CD relationship is presented to the relevant professional, there should be no doubt that there is a heightened risk of a rapid developing substance misuse issue.

To summarise these models is quite straightforward:

ADHD is an independent risk factor for problematic drug use, but the combination of ADHD and conduct disorder has the highest risk.

This summary segways into the debate regarding self-medication for people with ADHD and in the next element of this book I shall seek to examine this theory and illustrate the rationale and propensity for such action.

Self-medication

The notion of self-medication is an appealing theory regarding drug abuse. Glass[6] wrote that, 'drug abuse begins as a partially successful attempt to assuage painful feelings. Individuals, predisposed by biological or psychological vulnerabilities find that drug effects corresponding to their particular problems are powerfully reinforcing'.

But how does self-medication actually manifest in practice? What do all the words of the academics mean in real life? To answer these questions we should really look at real life examples.

The following case example is taken from the work conducted with Alistair Roy. The case study is from interviews in the summer of 2006 with people who had been in drug treatment and unusually, were members of a peer support group that recognised their ADHD as a contributory factor to their problems with drugs. Only the names of the individuals have been changed in the text.

Paul

Paul gave his testimony so that we can encourage better and more effective practices in drug services that support drug users with ADHD.

His difficulties began at school where he found the classroom difficult, he had problems sitting still and following the teacher's instructions . . .

---

[5] Flory, K et al (2003) Clinical Child and Family Psychology Review, 2003—Springer, No. 1.
[6] Glass R M (1992).

"I didn't like the classroom; I didn't like people telling me what to do. I wasn't diagnosed then and I didn't know what it was and they were saying my mum's not disciplining me enough."

Paul was labelled by teachers and other parents; he started missing school at 11 years of age, spending time with young people older than himself. Paul resented the teachers blaming his mum for his behaviour, he felt misunderstood, unsupported and ostracised. Although at the time he hadn't recognised the cause of missing school, now Paul looks back and sees that he was just refusing to go to school.

Now mixing with an older age group, Paul began using cannabis; this made him feel accepted by this new peer group. It is my suggestion that the resentment within Paul, the feeling of being excluded and then seeking friendship with an older age group, was the first indicator of a tipping point for those around him . . .

"because I messed about with older people I was always with an older age group and when they were smoking I just smoked to be with them."

Cannabis brought about some changes in Paul's life, especially with regard to how he felt about himself, it affected the way he felt around other people and how they interacted with him.

"It just seemed to relax us and no one seemed to bother me when I was relaxed, because I wasn't moving about and all that, it calmed me down. But as soon as it started to wear off it seemed like my head was on a motor again and I was off."

The effects, both in terms of his peer group acceptance and the temporary reduction in his hyperactive behaviour, reinforced the benefits to Paul for continued use of cannabis, but as this tale amplifies, in circumstances like Paul's, the likelihood of escalation to more powerful drugs was likely, and did occur at the age of 13 when Paul was offered and used heroin.

"It all started with the ADHD, and because of my height I was small and all that, I used to think 'oh well, if I take this, I won't bother what anyone says now'. 'Cos little things like that used to get to me head and they would just play over and over in me head. But now I am not really bothered, but then I was. So I'd take the heroin to stop me head going and forget what people were saying."

But, the frequent and continued use of heroin did not dissolve all of Paul's problems as he hoped they would. When his issues returned they came back in a worse state than they were before, and as can be expected by the casual observer to this tale, Paul's problematic drug use put an enormous strain on his family relationships. At the age of 14,

> Paul was placed into local authority care and taken into secure accommodation, his heroin use rapidly built up to a daily dependency.
>
> *"When I was 15 that's when I really started to get on the smack and it all just changed from there . . . my family life . . . I fucked it right up being on that smack."*
>
> Between the ages of 18 and 20 Paul had 8 custodial prison sentences, and during this period, when he was twenty, he lost his father. His inheritance was £42,000 which he received on his 21st birthday, in 8 weeks he had spent it all on heroin and crack cocaine.
>
> Paul is now out of prison, in treatment for his addictions and receiving assistance from the specific provision of an ADHD support group.

This sad tale, and it is a sad tale, highlights many issues, and I would ask the reader to contemplate how many key contact opportunities were missed in Paul's younger years and at what stage was his 'tipping point', where strongly led, powerful interventions may have altered the trajectory of this man's life. Paul has survived this; many do not, the lack of survival manifesting in many different ways, e.g. financially, emotionally or physically.

The case study combined with the leading academic research tells us a number of things:

- There is normally a profound tendency for the young person with ADHD to feel excluded from their peer group
- There is a frequently found pathway into alcohol and drug use to 'fit in'
- This strategy has a short lifespan of effectiveness, it only works for a while
- Problems don't dissolve, they float to the surface again

When looking for signs of the 'tipping point' a clue to possible prevalence comes from Milberger and colleagues who followed 6–17 year olds with and without ADHD for 4 years, and found that ADHD was specifically associated with a higher risk for initiating cigarette smoking even after controlling for social class, psychiatric co-morbidity, and intelligence (Milberger, Biederman, Faraone, Chen, & Jones, 1996). Pomerleau[7] found in 1995 that 40% of adults with ADHD smoked, against a figure in the general population of only 26%.

Following on from cigarette smoking, other commentators such as Barkley and Wilens point to a pathway of more rapid onset of substance abuse, as I outlined earlier.

---

[7] Pomerleau, OF, Downey, KK, Stelson, FW, Pomerleau, CS (1995). *Cigarette smoking in adult patients diagnosed with Attention Deficit Hyperactivity Disorder.* Journal of Substance Abuse.

Treatment regimens

The purpose of any treatment for an addiction, in this case the discussion centres on drugs, is to pull the addict away from the lifestyle and problems of addiction and to then 'normalise' to a point of relative self-sufficiency free from dependency. Treatment for substance abuse, therefore, should have a focus on the needs of the individual and build a programme that is bespoke to accurately determined needs. This is where I believe treatment in the UK falls down.

Wilson and Levin[8] found that adults with ADHD actually struggle to maintain substance misuse programmes and it is acknowledged that for those with ADHD, more informed treatment for the condition can reduce the risk of relapse.

A key question that I am asked is 'why is this?' There are simple answers that when read look straightforward, however, they don't reveal the true complexity of the debate and I recognise that the co-morbid ADHD / problematic drug use cohort presents an extremely intricate set of issues. However, those reasons may include:

- People with ADHD behave in a way that confuses staff at treatment centres
- These sufferers have often had long-term feelings of rejection and are marginalised more that others
- Attendance at clinics is difficult in itself and is then compounded by time management issues and extension of frustrations about not being understood
- To disengage or to be asked to leave the treatment programme is a common norm.

The ADHD sufferer/problematic drug user therefore tends to run into a pattern of longer relapse with shorter recovery periods, and generally there are few avenues to turn to for relevant assistance. Entry into a drug treatment programme could be seen as another 'tipping point', whereby with a relatively low cost additional intervention, such as a simple ADHD screen, professionals delivering these services could identify a subgroup of sufferers and begin to recognise a unique set of needs. Once more the identification of the key contact opportunity is without a great challenge, but common sense is rarely common practice, especially in the complex world of dual diagnosis of ADHD and problematic drug use.

---

[8] Jeffery Wilson and Frances Levin. (2005) Journal of child and adolescent psychopharmacology, vol. 15.

Treatment models

I would argue that conventional models for treatment require extensions to existing protocols to seek further success in this arena. In all of the work undertaken with Ali Roy, we have yet to truly discover a drug treatment model that offers end to end satisfaction for the person who has ADHD. Given the figures for drug related deaths in the UK, there should be no complacency over this subject:

> Between 1993 and 2004, there were 12,687 male deaths and 3,041 female deaths relating to drug misuse.[9]

Ali and I worked with professionals from Norway, the Netherlands, Belgium, Italy and the US amongst others, and from that work it is suggested that models for treatment should be built on three stages, (1) the baseline (2) treatment and (3) post treatment. Furthermore, the components of such a model should be seen as a continuum of care, seamlessly providing a wraparound service for the young people who entrust themselves to the professional disciplines concerned.

The baseline of assessment

The pathology that walks through the door for a presenting drug user is one of a unique set of circumstances and these should be seen and recognised as such. The attributes of low self-esteem, feeling marginalised and being misunderstood should be expected in a high number of the cohort. A person's ability to maximise on the offered services will be determined to some extent by their attributes and whether or not they are understood. There is no fixed model for this form of treatment due to the complexity of the subject matter, but there are key elements to the process and these should provide common threads to progress.

- Key element—accepting the unique nature of the presenting case
- Looking for the previous history of 'tipping points' and failed key contact opportunities, and using these as learning outcomes for future interventions.

Treatment

People accessing treatment for problems with drugs, should be assessed as thoroughly as possible, and if this means an extension to current provisions then so be it. Experience from Norway and the Netherlands, where different models of treatment are practised to those in the UK, suggest that a full psychological assessment is a 'must do' for successful outcomes to be expected. This normally takes the form of clinical interview, self-assessment, and

---

[9] Office for national statistics. (2006).

parental and school reports where available. The focus is not on a particular disorder such as ADHD, but for full assessment of psychological health.

There is a belief within practitioners in the UK drug services field that people who suffer problematic drug use should not be treated for a mental health disorder with stimulants. Both Norway and the Netherlands treat ADHD / problematic drug use with stimulant medication. Where some observers believe this may 'hook' the patient onto prescribed medications, quite the opposite has been found to be the case. . . .

> "*Our experience was that these patients were not hanging on the medicine door asking for their medicine, not at all, it was we that had to run after them.*"[10]

With careful screening, relevant assessment and professional diagnosis, coupled with prescribing vigilance, European evidence suggests that it is possible to use stimulant medication as one important feature of treating this complex problem. As many of the people I have interviewed have informed me, once their ADHD was appropriately managed it was easier for them to accept other services and take full part in drug programmes.

Our European colleagues also advocate a strong and managed physical regime for any programme participant. Experience from Norway suggests that an addiction to jogging can form and this becomes a healthier form of desire than the drug related alternative.

Finally, the ADHD related treatment programmes that I have examined make effective use of group work and coaching. But there is a definite caveat to this, the participants must be aware of, and fully understand, the behavioural patterns of people with ADHD for this to succeed and for engagement to survive over time.

There are key elements to this stage:

- Structured programmes are beneficial to this population, people with ADHD perform well under a system that provides scaffolding and support
- Rigour at the assessment stage, with psychological assessment as a key element, have proven benefits
- The use of medication for people with ADHD should not be seen as negative, European evidence suggests this can and does work

Post treatment

Aftercare is vitally important for the successful reintegration of people with ADHD / problematic drug use. It is often the case that services fail to recognise this, and in doing so take little account of personal circumstances and the structural disadvantages this population have.

---

[10] A N Roy (2005) Taken from an interview with staff at the Bergan Clinic, Norway.

Becoming 'clean' then moving forward into a lifestyle that has no consideration of the possible, if not probable causes of the slide into problems with drugs is a recipe for recidivism.

My suggestions for aftercare may appear obvious, but they are seen as expensive, resource intensive and given that some of the target audience may have already been in treatment and not sustained a healthy lifestyle, they may not appear 'worthy' of this level of intervention; the 'lost cause' syndrome.

- Mentoring by trained staff, trained in ADHD and its unique requirements for the patient
- Peer led support / buddying, proven to be acceptable if the understanding of the ADHD is there, this has advantages for both participants in terms of motivation and therefore longer-term results
- The continuance and monitoring of physical activity
- Approaches that examine, understand, and react accordingly to family / home life situations—the context for the sufferer's life.

The key elements for treatment are:

- Treatment must 'wrap around' the individual, as an individual
- All the people involved **must** understand ADHD and its associated behaviours
- There must be interventions to change the context of life that may serve to frustrate the continuance of success.

I firmly believe that Scarlett's life story sums up all that there is to be discussed in this chapter of the book, her story is detailed in full at appendix 2, but in a nutshell;

> Scarlett failed at school, was ostracised from family and school. She turned to alcohol, then 'harder' drugs and began to 'totally screw up her life'. After many misdiagnosis and time as an adult in psychiatric services, often involuntarily, she was picked up by a social worker who correctly believed Scarlett had ADHD. She is now running her own photography business, and the people that made the key intervention still care for her welfare.

Chapter eight

ADHD and road use

AT THE TIME of writing this book I was a serving police officer, and at the start of this work, as I said earlier, I had a responsibility to reduce crime; I did not have a corporate responsibility to reduce road casualties. So imagine the setting, I am sitting in an assistant chief constable's office trying to convince her that the ADHD and road 'thing' is something we should get into. Assistant chief constables are quite high up the management ladder, in fact, very high up the ladder, and conversations with this rank were rare at this stage of my career, especially conversations where I was leading the agenda. This is my recollection of the relevant content of the meeting:

ACC "So I don't get it, what is the connection between ADHD and driving?"

PA "I don't see what there isn't to get, there is a connection to driving stand-ards."

ACC "Convince me . . ."

PA "You take a fast car, any car is a fast car, then put someone who struggles to concentrate, who acts impulsively and is extremely hyperactive behind the wheel, alone, on our roads . . . (I was about to continue)"

ACC "OK, I get it!"

And really, that's as basic as the debate needs to be, especially as a 'starter for ten'. But there is a lot of science behind this subject and it's worth explor-ing, especially as it is difficult sometimes to actually grasp the severity of the problem enough to stop youngsters putting themselves at incredible risk by using the roads. And this debate is not all about cars for the 17 plus teen-agers. Kids on foot, skateboards, roller blades, scooters, bicycles, mopeds, all the available forms of road transport are in this debate, so it applies to all kids from the moment they walk without holding hands. Children's safety in the road environment is an important practical issue.

There is an obvious starting point for the discussion, that being that children do not assess danger as effectively as adults. Hill[1] found that even the youngest of children demonstrated a rudimentary concept of danger and this developed with age, it was very low when compared with adults. Although that aspect of science will not place people in rockets bound for another galaxy, it is important that we grasp the fact that children do not and will not

---

[1] Hill, R (2000) *Young Children's Concepts of Danger* British Journal of Developmental Psychology . Vol. 18.

appreciate danger like an adult. Now couple onto that the behavioural aspects of ADHD and we have a problem, in fact we have an understated, large problem. And it is one that affects lots of families each and every year.

Another study by Hill[2], who incidentally carried out this research in the UK, found that children who were better at maintaining concentration when challenged by a distracting event, crossed the road in a safer manner.

DiScala[3] studied injuries to children and compared results of children with and without ADHD, and she found that children with ADHD were more likely to be injured as pedestrians or cyclists than those not suffering from ADHD and that their injuries would be more severe. German government research found that 14 year old children with ADHD were nine times more likely to have a pedestrian accident than those without. So it appears quite clear that there is additional risk for young people with ADHD who use our roads, from the formative pedestrian years through to the use of motor vehicles which I will examine next before coming onto what can be done, in practical terms, about these issues.

Driving and ADHD

Russ Barkley's work with extended, longitudinal studies of people with ADHD has led to some remarkable findings, and on this subject I find Russ both passionate and extremely informative. Without reservation I will refer to his findings during this section of my work, both in presentations, meetings and this book.

Driving presents a challenge for anyone, and driving a car is a truly useful way to describe the conscious competence model I used earlier in chapter 6. At first we aren't really aware we cannot drive, then we are, then we realise we can do it, then we just 'do it' naturally. Or do we, or rather can people with ADHD successfully migrate to the conscious competence stage, the third stage, a consideration before we attempt to examine the unconscious competence stages of this useful model?

Barkley found that people with ADHD demonstrated many problems operating a motor car, he found more fixed penalty tickets were issued, there were more disqualifications and the accident rate was higher. In the self-reporting aspects of his work he found:

---

[2] Hill, R et al (2001) *Children's attentional skills and road behaviour* British Journal of Developmental Psychology. Vol. 7.
[3] Di Scala, C (1998) *Injuries to children with ADHD*. PEDIATRICS Vol. 102 No. 6 December 1998.

- Higher levels in the number of the ADHD group that had driven before they were old enough
- The ADHD group had been given 12 or more fixed penalty tickets
- The drivers with ADHD had higher incidents of speeding fines, and
- They had been involved in five or more collisions.

Studies in New Zealand[4] report that the incidents are as prevalent in women as men, therefore we must see this as an issue for every child with ADHD, not just the obviously hyperactive boys. If we refer back to the work on executive functioning in chapter 6 we see how the requirements to concentrate, often cited as a female ADHD character trait, is as important to success as controlling impulsivity, and this is never more so than in road usage.

Perhaps the most effective way to highlight the facts regarding driving is a table of results from Barkley's Milwaukee studies:

Poorer steering, more braking mistakes and slower reactions to significant events	
Use fewer safe driving techniques	
More likely to drive before legally licensed	
More collisions where the driver is at fault 2.3, vs 1.2 times	
Higher number of collisions	% with 2 or more, 40 vs 6 % with 3 or more, 26 vs 9
More speeding tickets, 4.5 vs 1.2	
More prone to having injury (i.e. more severe) collisions, 60 vs 17	
More disqualifications, 2.2 vs 0.7	

Elsewhere, Barkley states that drivers with ADHD are four times more likely to have a car crash. This is a significant figure as it is the same figure for people who hold and use their mobile phone whilst driving, perhaps that puts this issue into a perspective that we can relate to? This is the same ratio that brought legislation into Britain to ban the use of mobile telephones whilst driving.

Encouraging safer driving

Responding to the challenges and worries parents and carers of youngsters with ADHD have each time inexperienced drivers are behind the wheel

---

[4] Nada-Raja et al *Inattentive and hyperactive behaviors and driving offences in adolescence.* Journal of the American Academy of Child and Adolescent Psychiatry.

Marlene Snyder carried out extensive research to find solutions. In her book, 'ADHD & Driving: A Guide for Parents of Teens with AD/HD', she outlines her findings, for example, one activity provides a website for measuring aggressiveness on the road. When both parent and teen complete the activity, they are both reported to learn not only about themselves but also more about each other.

I was fortunate to be able to work with Marlene and to obtain her blessing for adapting her work into a ten point advice leaflet for parents; this has been paraphrased in appendix 3. The most important factor I can take from this plan relates to medication, most importantly encouraging parents and carers to understand the medication that their child is taking. To expand on this aspect of road safety I refer to the published work of Dan Cox, from the University of Virginia, again I was fortunate to work with Dan and I have found his work to be enlightening.

Dan Cox's work[5] reviewed different medication efficacy against each other, in simple terms he wanted to know if a longer acting ADHD medication had a greater or lesser effect on driving standards than a medication taken three times a day. His published results make interesting reading and although I would not wish to get embroiled in debate regarding which medication is 'best', or the merits of medication over alternative forms of therapy, past studies have shown that stimulants commonly used to treat ADHD can help improve driving performance among this group. There are many different formulations of stimulant drugs to treat ADHD and parents need to know the effect of one over the other, and to know in detail the consequences of the medication their child takes.

In previous studies, Dan Cox found that a slow release methylphenidate compound when compared with immediate release methylphenidate was better at improving driving performance. He did this by using a driving simulator; teenage drivers, between 16 and 19 years of age, displayed their driving skills after taking slow release medication, immediate release medication or a placebo. Study participants took their medications at 8 a.m. They came to the driving simulator laboratory and completed 15-minute simulated drives at 5 p.m., 8 p.m. and 11 p.m. Their driving performance was determined by sophisticated computer algorithms which led to Dan's findings.

Researchers found that treatments with slow release medication led to fewer inattentive driving errors and less hyperactive or impulsive driving errors such as speeding and inappropriate braking, compared with other medication delivery mechanisms and the placebo.

---

[5] Cox, D (2004) *Impact of Methylphenidate Delivery Profiles on Driving Performance of Adolescents With Attention-Deficit/Hyperactivity Disorder: A Pilot Study.* Journal of the American Academy of Child and Adolescent Psychiatry. March 2004.

So what is the key message for carers and parents? Quite simply put I would state that:

The fact that your child is taking medication for their ADHD does not in itself equate to totally managed behaviour and safety. Check the efficacy of the medication, and if necessary call a halt to road use if the effects are likely to have worn off. Your psychiatrist can assist you with this information.

Chapter nine

Tipping Points

WITHOUT ANY doubt the concept of 'tipping points' dovetails very effectively into the arguments put forward as key contact opportunities. It has been quite an experience to deliver presentations to parents of children with ADHD, pointing out during the event how 'tipping points' can be recognised and how important it is **at that point and no later,** to intervene immediately and to good effect to prevent negative outcomes. The realisation that opportunities were missed and that they may have contributed to the situation being experienced, usually a negative outcome, has been harsh for some and I imagine will continue to be so. But exactly where in the continuum of a young person's life would we expect to find 'tipping points'?

The initial question should be 'exactly what is a 'tipping point''?

Tipping Points are those times in a young person's life where if an appropriate and timely intervention is not made, the person concerned has a higher than average chance of going forward into a life that has negative and harmful outcomes. Any interventions should be informed, made with a clear set of objectives and mindful of the particular circumstances appertaining to the young person concerned.

School life

Initial signs for a tipping point should come from interaction with peers and a shift toward rejection and group exclusion.

Running in parallel with group interactions are the interactions with teachers, particularly a teacher's attitude toward the individual pupil. *Anecdotally, following an observed teaching session where the teacher had reported having difficulties with one pupil who was demonstrating ADHD characteristics, in the de-brief the observer asked the teacher how many times he had spoken to the child in a negative way; to the answer of 'none' the observer corrected him and informed him it was 30 plus. The teacher had become so used to 'nagging' the child he was no longer seeing this as an occurrence of note and was unaware of the affect this could have on the child.*

The switch to secondary education from junior school, the transition as it is sometimes called, presents the child who has ADHD with particular problems and challenges. *Instead of teachers attending the classroom, effectively bringing the day to the child, the child now has different classes in different rooms and not always with the same teacher or the same group of pupils. Evidence suggests this is a point in time where children with ADHD can get confused, get repeatedly chastised and become negative to the school process. Mentors are one example of how this issue can be overcome with little investment financially.*

Adolescence

Mixing with older children, having been excluded from the natural age related peer group is, as discussed in chapter seven (ADHD and drugs), a very important tipping point that needs to be caught.

Exclusion, whether temporary or permanent, from school, should provide professionals with a 'heads up' that something is going wrong, but the need to recognise and intervene as described above as a tipping point is often missed.

Early and continued smoking of cigarettes offers any parent or carer an early warning that the child with ADHD is embarking on a pathway, described in detail in this book, that is likely to lead to a higher than average risk of problematic drug use.

Entry into the criminal justice system, through minor disorder, a caution for petty theft or going missing from either the home or care establishment, are classic tipping points. It is ultimately extremely important for children with ADHD to be fully understood at this stage of their lives and that anything professionals do from this point forward follows the model as described above.

Academic achievement, or rather difficulties with achievement, often demoralise any child, but again, if this is on the back of all the other school based issues above, it can and often is worse for the ADHD child. *Further complications come from the fact that ADHD can lead to difficulties in learning which are often, mistakenly, interpreted as an inability to learn. The two things are completely different, having ADHD does not indicate that a child is educationally challenged, some of the brightest pupils have been found to have this disorder and it is for the teaching profession to recognise these issues and separate them out.*

Young adulthood

The first job often gives rise to a tipping point that is hard to recognise. If the reader was to recall the disorientation they felt in their first real job and then transpose that into the life of the child with ADHD and all its associated problems with isolation, withdrawal and feelings of general incompetence we can quickly ascertain how this can serve to reinforce feelings that may have arisen or lain dormant from school days. *Although it is not always realistic to expect employers to recognise their responsibilities initially, the issues are real, and maybe, just maybe, an employer would like to know before issues arise that there is some potential for this?*

Tipping points can occur at any time, but they can be spotted if they are being looked for. If they are not being looked for I am confident they will not be found. For the lives of the children with ADHD we are discussing, that is a tragedy. Preventing those tragic outcomes has motivated me to write this book, it is my fervent hope that by reading it you may be more sensitised to the needs of this population of young people. They represent our futures and demonstrate our successes, or lack of, as professionals charged with a responsibility to ensure they get the best start on their journey toward achieving their life potential.

Appendices

Appendix 1—Myths about ADHD

Becky Booth, Wilma Fellman, LPC, Judy Greenbaum, Ph.D., Terry Matlen, ACSW, Geraldine Markel, Ph.D., Howard Morris, Arthur L. Robin, Ph.D., Angela Tzelepis, Ph.D.

The following myths—and factual responses—have been collected from rebuttals to recent media articles about ADD/ADHD. The rebuttals were written by MAAAN (Metro Area Adult ADHD Network, based in the Detroit area).

Myth #1: ADHD is a "phantom disorder".

FACT: The existence of a neurobiological disorder is not an issue to be decided by the media through public debate, but rather as a matter of scientific research. Scientific studies spanning 95 years, summarized in the professional writings of Dr. Russell Barkley, Dr. Sam Goldstein and others, have consistently identified a group of individuals who have trouble with concentration, impulse control, and in some cases, hyperactivity. Although the name given to this group of individuals, our understanding of them, and the estimated prevalence of this group, has changed a number of times over the past six decades, the symptoms have consistently been found to cluster together. Currently called Attention Deficit Hyperactivity Disorder, this syndrome has been recognized as a disability by the courts, the United States Department of Education, the Office for Civil Rights, the United States Congress, the National Institutes of Health, and all major professional medical, psychiatric, psychological and educational associations.

Myth #2: Ritalin is like cocaine, and the failure to give youngsters drug holidays from Ritalin causes them to develop psychosis.

FACT: Methylphenidate (Ritalin) is a medically prescribed stimulant medication that is chemically different from cocaine. The therapeutic use of methylphenidate does NOT CAUSE addiction or dependence, and does not lead to psychosis. Some children have such severe ADHID symptoms that it can be dangerous for them to have a medication holiday, for example a child who is so hyper and impulsive that they will run into traffic without stopping to look first. Hallucinations are an extremely rare side effect of methylphenidate, and their occurrence has nothing to do with the presence or absence of medication holidays. Individuals with ADHD who are properly treated with stimulant medication such as Ritalin have a lower risk of developing problems with alcohol and other drugs than the general population.

More importantly, 50 years of research has repeatedly shown that children, adolescents, and adults with ADHD safely benefit from treatment with methylphenidate.

Myth #3: No study has ever demonstrated that taking stimulant medications can cause any lasting behavioural or educational benefit to ADHD children.

FACT: Research has repeatedly shown that children, adolescents and adults with ADHD benefit from therapeutic treatment with stimulant medications, which has been used safely and studied for more than 50 years. For example, The New York Times reviewed a recent study from Sweden showing positive long-term effects of stimulant medication therapy on children with ADHD. Readers interested in more studies on the effectiveness of medication with ADHD should consult the professional writings of Dr. Russell Barkley, Drs. Gabrielle Weiss and Lily Hechtman, and Dr. Joseph Biederman.

Myth #4: ADHD kids are learning to make excuses, rather than take responsibility for their actions.

FACT: Therapists, educators and physicians routinely teach children that ADHD is a challenge, not an excuse. Medication corrects their underlying chemical imbalance, giving them a fair chance of facing the challenges of growing up to become productive citizens. Accommodations for the disabled, as mandated by legislation are not ways of excusing them from meeting society's responsibilities, but rather make it possible for them to compete on a levelled playing field.

Myth #5: ADHD is basically due to bad parenting and lack of discipline, and all that ADHD children really need is old-fashioned discipline, not any of these phoney therapies.

FACT: There are still some parent-bashers around who believe the century old anachronism that child misbehaviour is always a moral problem of the 'bad child'. Under this model, the treatment has been to "beat the Devil out of the child." Fortunately, most of us are more enlightened today. A body of family interaction research conducted by Dr. Russell Barkley and others has unequivocally demonstrated that simply providing more discipline without any other interventions worsens rather than improves the behaviour of children with ADHD. One can't make a paraplegic walk by applying discipline. Similarly, one can't make a child with a biologically based lack of self-control act better by simply applying discipline alone.

Myth #6: Ritalin is unsafe, causing serious weight loss, mood swings, Tourette's syndrome, and sudden, unexplained deaths.

FACT: Research has repeatedly shown that children, adolescents, and adults with ADHD benefit from treatment with Ritalin (also known as methylphenidate), which has been safely used for approximately 50 years. There are NO published cases of deaths from overdoses of Ritalin; if you take too much Ritalin, you will feel terrible and act strangely for a few hours, but you will not die. This cannot be said about many other medications. The unexplained deaths cited in some articles are from a combination of Ritalin and other drugs, not from Ritalin alone. Further investigation of those cases has revealed that most of the children had unusual medical problems which contributed to their deaths. It is true that many children experience appetite loss and some moodiness or 'rebound effect' when Ritalin wears off. A very small number of children may show some temporary tics, but these do not become permanent. Ritalin does not permanently alter growth, and usually does not result in weight loss. Ritalin does not cause Tourette's syndrome, rather many youngsters with Tourette's also have ADHD. In some cases, Ritalin even leads to an improvement of the tics in children who have ADHD and Tourette's.

Myth #7: Teachers around the country routinely push pills on any students who are even a little inattentive or overactive.

FACT: Teachers are well meaning individuals who have the best interests of their students in mind. When they see students who are struggling to pay attention and concentrate, it is their responsibility to bring this to parents' attention, so parents can take appropriate action. The majority of teachers do not simply push pills, they provide information so that parents can seek out appropriate diagnostic help. We do agree with the position that teachers should not diagnose ADHD. However, being on the front line with children, they collect information, raise the suspicion of ADHD, and bring the information to the attention of parents, who then need to have a full evaluation conducted outside the school. The symptoms of ADHD must be present in school and at home before a diagnosis is made; teachers do not have access to sufficient information about the child's functioning to make a diagnosis of ADHD, or for that matter to make any kind of medical diagnosis.

Myth #8:   Efforts by teachers to help children who have attentional problems can make more of a difference than medications such as Ritalin.

FACT: It would be nice if this were true, but recent scientific evidence from the multi-modal treatment trials sponsored by the National Institute of Mental Health suggests it is a myth. In these studies, stimulant medication alone was compared to stimulant medication plus a multi-modal psychological and educational treatment, as treatments for children with ADHD. The scientists found that the multi-modal treatment plus the medication was not much better than the medication alone. Teachers and therapists need to continue to do everything they can to help individuals with ADHD, but we need to realize that if we don't also alter the biological factors that affect ADHD, we won't see much change.

Myth #9: CH.A.D.D. is supported by drug companies, and along with many professionals, are simply in this field to make a quick buck from ADHD.

FACT: Thousands of parents and professionals volunteer countless hours daily to over 600 chapters of CH.A.D.D. around the U.S. and Canada on behalf of individuals with ADHD. CH.A.D.D. is very open about disclosing any contributions from drug companies. These contributions only support the organization's national conference, which consists of a series of educational presentations, 95% of which are on topics other than medications. None of the local chapters receive any of this money. It is a disgrace to impugn the honesty and efforts of all of these dedicated volunteers. CH.A.D.D. supports all known effective treatments for ADHD, including medication, and takes positions against unproven and costly remedies.

Myth #10: It is not possible to accurately diagnose ADD or ADHD in children or adults.

FACT: Although scientists have not yet developed a single medical test for diagnosing ADHD, clear-cut clinical diagnostic criteria have been developed, researched and refined over several decades. The current generally accepted diagnostic criteria for ADHD are listed in the Diagnostic and Statistical Manual of Mental Disorders (DSM-IV), published by the American Psychiatric Association (1995). Using these criteria and multiple methods to collect comprehensive information from multiple informants, ADHD can be reliably diagnosed in children and adults.

Myth #11: Children outgrow ADD or ADHD.

FACT: ADHD is not found just in children. We have learned from a number of excellent follow-up studies conducted over the past few decades that ADHD often lasts a lifetime. Over 70% of children diagnosed as having ADHD will continue to manifest the full clinical syndrome in adolescence, and 15–50% will continue to manifest the full clinical syndrome in adulthood. If untreated, individuals with ADHD may develop a variety of secondary problems as they move through life, including depression, anxiety, substance abuse, academic failure, vocational problems, marital discord, and emotional distress. If properly treated, most individuals with ADHD live productive lives and cope reasonably well with their symptoms.

Myth #12: Methylphenidate prescriptions in the U.S. have increased by 600%.

FACT: The production quotas for methylphenidate increased 6-fold; however that DEA production quota is a gross estimate based on a number of factors, including FDA estimates of need, drug inventories at hand, exports, and industry sales expectations. One cannot conclude that a 6-fold increase in production quotas translates to a 6-fold, increase in the use of methylphenidate among U.S. children any more than one should conclude that Americans eat 6 times more bread because U.S. wheat production increased 6-fold even though much of the grain is stored for future use and export to countries that have no wheat production. Further, of the approximately 3.5 million children who meet the criteria for ADHD, only about 50% of them are diagnosed and have stimulant medication included in their treatment plan. The estimated number of children taking methylphenidate for ADD suggested in some media stories, fails to note that methylphenidate is also prescribed for adults who have ADHD, people with narcolepsy, and geriatric patients who receive considerable benefit from it for certain conditions associated with old age, such as memory functioning (see Paediatrics, December 1996, Vol. 98, No. 6).

Appendix 2—Scarlett's story

"When I was growing up, I just knew there was something wrong with me but I couldn't figure it out."

This introduction to Scarlett's life story is an all too common statement from adults who, when they look back on their lives, realise they had ADHD but neither they nor anyone else were able to identify and tackle it correctly.

Scarlett had a hard time at school; in fact she had a hard time with her friends, parents and her own feelings. In general life didn't appear as easy for her as it did for her friends and family. She knew in some way that she was different, and this difference was one of the contributing factors to the beginning of the downward spiral of low self-esteem; a problem at the root of much dysfunction in person's life.

Labeled as a disruptive pupil, criticized for not applying herself and consistently being informed that she would not live up to her potential, Scarlett remembers school with emotional pain. Suspended for being disruptive, Scarlett found herself without proper support and adrift with no one trying to determine her problem. She did have loving parents, but ADHD was not something that came to mind in the 70's, especially with girls who were not hyper-active.

Learning was very hard, and "teachers never presented information in a way that my brain could wrap around." The search for an easy way of learning just didn't materialize and this became a problem. Her constant search for ways of learning led to a continual barrage of questions to her teachers, making her appear, in her words, like an 'idiot" to her peers. The natural alternative became her norm and Scarlett withdrew to a point of silence and pretence that she understood the classroom learning. Many opportunities to learn were lost.

Looking back she recognizes that she was in a period of sensory overload, struggling with inattentiveness and being distracted. Her environment affected her. Sounds, smells and people were continual negative diversions for her. The only time Scarlett could manage to concentrate was when the subject was something she was really interested in and was also good at. The combination made her feel unusually good about herself, but life rarely works that way.

During her college years, Scarlett continued to run into difficulties. Alcohol remained a prop of life, as did unlawful drugs. There was no diagnosis of the "problem" and therefore no professional understanding and help. Her lifestyle and emotional problems led to a suicide attempt before her 20th birthday.

Only at the age of 30 did Scarlett receive the diagnosis of ADHD, but there were still problems due to the psychiatrist's unwillingness to treat her with stimulant medication due to her history of alcohol and drug abuse.

After almost 7 years of drug recovery and abstinence from alcohol, she continued to struggle, knowing there was something still "wrong." Incorrect medication with drugs not focused on her ADHD led her back to alcoholism, fed a depression and set the stage for an inevitable entrance into an inappropriate marriage which ultimately ended in divorce.

During the marriage, and 5 years after the ADHD diagnosis, a new physician placed Scarlett on a suitable medication programme. It was too late to save the marriage, but from that point on she recalls feeling like "my life changed, it was that fast. I was let out of my cage."

Scarlett wishes to go on the record in this book as stating that for far too long she suffered in silence. People with illnesses such as cancer do not have their peers turn on them and demand that they snap out of it, as she did with her ADHD.

In her words again, "ADHD is an illness like any other, but it's an "invisible disability" in many ways which unfortunately leads many people in society to believe it's not a real illness with serious and long-term life consequences. This only adds to the suffering an untreated ADHD individual already lives with each day. This is the main reason alcohol, drugs, deviant behavior etc. become options. They are all ways to self-medicate and stop the pain."

To this day Scarlett attends meetings of Alcoholics Anonymous and receives cognitive behavioural therapy (CBT) which is assisting her to abandon her previous inappropriate coping mechanisms for ADHD, and is leading her to a better life. Medication is also still an important part of her recovery.

Scarlett wasn't able to stick with anything prior top her diagnosis and she was failing to produce success in her work world until her diagnosis and treatment with the proper medication. She is now extremely successful, delightful company and she is, without any doubt, making something of her life; a life she nearly took away from herself and her family.

In writing this case study with Scarlett, I cannot fail to ask myself how many tipping points were missed in her life? I also reflect on how lucky some professionals, as well as the individuals are that failures to understand the warning signs didn't lead to dire consequences.

Appendix 3—ADHD and driving—advice for parents

1. Display good adult driving habits.

Your children and passengers in your car have observed your driving. They have watched your every action. Is it good enough to be a role model? Do you use your mobile phone while driving? Do you speed excessively? Would you be comfortable if your teenager drove as you do?

2. Determine the readiness of the learner to drive.

Young people with ADHD are often emotionally and functionally immature when compared to others of the same age. Teenagers with ADHD, therefore, may take significantly longer to develop good judgement and a mature attitude to driving. Teenagers who have explosive tempers, are uncooperative or cannot meet their current responsibilities are **not** ready to drive.

3. Ensure the learner driver fully understands the Highway Code.

This will ensure that the learner driver is aware of the rules of the road before they begin driving. They will also understand why these are the rules they are expected to obey.

4. Address ADHD and any other conditions or behaviour that impact on driving safely.

Learning to drive safely is a serious issue. When this is made more difficult by having ADHD the parents and the young learner driver must make efforts to understand these complications and work to minimise the risks involved.

5. Select driver education materials and plan the content of driving lessons.

When giving private driving lessons ensure that the lesson has been prepared beforehand. Ensure the instructor has the route planned and allotted a timescale to the lesson. The learner driver should also be prepared, ensuring they have taken any prescribed medication and are in a suitable mental and emotional condition to concentrate. If neither of these are in place, cancel the lesson.

6. Consider medication issues and driving safety.

Research has shown that ADHD behaviours can be significantly improved with medication use. Some of the known benefits include an increase in attention span and concentration. Individuals who have been prescribed medication should only drive within the time limits of the particular medication they are taking. Do you know what they are for your child's medication?

7. Establish an incentive scheme for ADHD drivers.

Parents of children with ADHD often use incentives to encourage their children to complete a particular task. Driving is no different. Some parents also state that driving is a powerful incentive to encourage everyday behaviour. Encourage your young person to work for the privilege of driving and the responsibility attached to it by developing a reward system.

8. Carry out the driving lesson plans.

It's common to underestimate the time needed to teach an individual to drive. A learner driver with ADHD will take **at least 3 times** longer to learn to drive. You should keep a log of hours and driving skills demonstrated during the lessons. This will enable you to check on progress and chart consistent faults. It will also allow the instructor to identify times of the day when the ADHD driver performs badly and provide lessons at a more appropriate time.

9. Discuss safe driving expectations with the ADHD driver.

Parents when considering whether to allow their child to drive should discuss the fact that there is a danger if they drink, smoke or use their mobile telephone whilst driving. If they insist they should not be allowed to begin driving.

10. Negotiate new rules after the ADHD driver has passed their test.

Having passed their test the new driver is ready to drive a car without adult supervision. Some new rules should be established before they drive alone:

- **Consider curfew times for weekdays and weekends in line with medication**
- **Discuss what times of day they can drive**
- **Discuss the consequences of an accident**
- **Restrict passengers totally if possible**
- **Keep a record of the persons driving**
- **Ensure they know what to do in an emergency**
- **Set rules for the use of the family car**
- **Include rewards for compliance**
- **Enforce no drinking and driving rules**
- **Determine who pays for petrol, insurance and driving tickets**

Appendix 4—Advice specifically for police officers regarding ADHD

This advice was originally written for a project in Lancashire. It never saw the light of day, but the advice still stands and is relevant. In preparing this advice I am indebted to ADDISS who agreed to its content, giving me the security and piece of mind to pass the work on.

What is ADHD?
How will I notice this in a person?
What does this mean to me as a police officer?
So, what do I do?
What happens if this person ends up in custody?
Interviewing an ADHD sufferer.

What is ADHD?

ADHD is a biological disorder that affects the functions of the brain. It is treatable, but not curable.

How will I notice this in a person?

There is no national identity card scheme for ADHD.

Sufferers of ADHD will normally have one or all of the following behaviour traits:—

- They will be hyperactive
- They cannot concentrate
- They act impulsively.

What does this mean to me as a police officer?

The person with ADHD will:

- Be likely to not respect your personal space
- Appear to you to be unnaturally aggressive
- Appear to you to be keen to get way from speaking to you.

So, what do I do?

Firstly, you must undertake all normal and reasonable steps to safeguard your own safety as in any confrontation with a member of the public.

Use the conflict resolution model to determine your approach. Remember, the person with ADHD may be confrontational, but may not be intentionally physically threatening. Verbal communication skills will probably calm the individual.

What happens if this person ends up in custody?

ADHD is a recognised mental disorder and therefore sufferers fall under the provisions of the Codes of Practice for mental health sufferers (Section C, 3.15). This means, despite everything you see and believe about this person they should:

- Have an appropriate adult with them (this may not necessarily be the parent or carer)
- Have special considerations regarding their rights, as ADHD sufferers often have problems with reading and writing
- Have special considerations in interviews (see below).

Those with ADHD are often prescribed medication that is designed to control their symptoms. When in custody, police officers and staff should ensure that they receive their medication as prescribed.

Interviewing an ADHD sufferer.

When interviewing a sufferer of ADHD, you should at all times:

- have an appropriate adult present
- avoid long, multiple and complicated questions
- avoid leading questions, people with ADHD are vulnerable to being easily led
- take regular breaks in the interview, people with ADHD have a short attention span and get bored and frustrated very easily—suggest a break every ten minutes
- recognise that inattention, impulsivity and being hyperactive in an interview are behavioural issues that greatly increase the risk of the person being vulnerable
- ensure that if an individual has been prescribed medication, that they have adhered to their prescription plan prior to any interview.

ADHD is often an ignored disorder in the justice system. It is your responsibility, when faced with the challenge of dealing with a sufferer, to get their welfare and the policing processes right, in accordance with PACE and the needs of the person.

Appendix 5—Advice for magistrates court staff

This advice was originally written for a project in Lancashire. It was used in Lancashire and has been distributed further by myself. In preparing this advice I am indebted to Tim Morris, a psychiatrist, who agreed to its content, giving me the confidence and piece of mind to pass the work on.

Attention Deficit and Hyperactivity Disorder (ADHD)— Good Practice Guide

This guide is relevant to those involved in criminal justice process (police, crown prosecution service, solicitors, witness support service, youth offending team and magistrates).

It will assist in the understanding of ADHD, aid recognition of the symptoms and encourage an appropriate response by those involved in that process.

What is ADHD?

ADHD was originally identified by a UK doctor in 1902, but is still relatively unknown in this country! Essentially it is a biological problem caused by a **chemical imbalance** in the brain and, as a biological problem that cannot be seen, is a hidden disability.

It is, however, recognised internationally as a disorder adversely affecting behaviour. Accordingly the ratio of those coming into contact with the criminal justice system and subject to prison sentences with ADHD, is thought to be disproportionately high.

There are three main types of behaviour that a person with ADHD may exhibit, namely:

- Inattentiveness
- Hyperactivity
- Impulsivity

A person with ADHD is more likely to exhibit this sort of behaviour when under pressure. Given that contact with the criminal justice system can create pressure, it is more likely to be apparent when he or she comes into contact with any part of the system. So from initial contact with the police, to charge, first appearance in court through to the final disposal decision and, on conviction, from the imposition of the sentence to completion and release, ADHD may manifest itself as follows:

Inattentiveness

A person with ADHD:

a) Often fails to give close attention to details or makes careless mistakes
b) Often has difficulty sustaining attention for long periods
c) Often does not seem to listen when spoken to directly
d) Often does not follow instructions, but not due to defiance or a failure to understand instructions
e) Often has difficulty in organising tasks and activities, including thoughts and responses to complicated questions
f) Often avoids, dislikes or is reluctant to engage in tasks that require sustained mental effort
g) Often loses things necessary for tasks or activities and is disorganised
h) Is frequently and easily distracted by extraneous stimuli, and struggles to return to the original task
i) Is often forgetful in daily activities

Hyperactivity

A person with ADHD:

a) Often fidgets with their hands or their feet or squirms in seat
b) Often seeks to leave their seat in the classroom or in other situations in which seating is expected
c) Often runs about or climbs excessively in situations in which it is inappropriate (in adolescents or adults, this may be limited to subjective feelings of restlessness)
d) Often has difficulty engaging in activities quietly
e) Is often 'on the go' or acts as if they are 'driven by motor'
f) Often talks excessively and is easily led in conversation.

Impulsivity

A person with ADHD:

a) Often blurts out answers before questions have been completed
b) Often has difficulty in waiting their turn
c) Often interrupts or intrudes on others (e.g. butts into conversations or thoughts).

What about treatment and medication?

ADHD cannot be cured, but with an effective combination of social support, structured lifestyle and, where appropriate, medication, ADHD can be treated and many people with ADHD lead productive lives.

The most commonly prescribed medical treatment for ADHD is in the form of a Class B drug, methylphenidate, a stimulant, appearing under the brand names of Ritalin, Ritalin SR, Equasym, Equasym XL, Medikinet or Concerta XL. A non stimulant medication known as Strattera may also be used. These drugs are prescribed by either a GP or a psychiatrist / paediatrician and those to whom it is prescribed are entitled to carry it and should, in the interest of just-ice, be allowed to continue taking it throughout the legal process even if they are held in custody. It will aid co-operation, understanding and compliance.

What can those involved in the criminal justice system do to assist the person with ADHD attending as a witness or defendant?

A person with ADHD may exhibit one or all of the above difficulties through-out the criminal justice process. He or she can be helped by:

1. Ensuring that, where necessary, an **appropriate adult** attends with him or her
2. Using language that he or she can understand
3. Checking that he or she has taken any prescribed medication and, if necessary, allowing him or her to take it
4. Keeping to appointment times and avoiding him or her waiting for long periods of time
5. Reading back anything you have written or repeating what has been said
6. Satisfying yourself that he or she understands all that is going on
7. Taking appropriate breaks in the appointment, proceedings or evidence.

A person with ADHD has great difficulty in organising their thoughts and attending to detail. They can rarely organise themselves well enough to get to appointments or court proceedings on time. Short-term memory problems mean that firstly they will forget the time, date and venue of an appointment. Secondly, if they do remember, they will begin the journey at the time they should be there. He or she can be helped by:

8. Telling him or her to attend 30 minutes prior to the time of the appoint-ment or proceedings and, as a consequence, building a period of toler-ance were he or she to be late
9. Asking their appropriate adult to take note of the date, time and venue of any appointment or court appearance, remind him or her of that date and time and assist him or her to attend as required

A person with ADHD has problems with complex, verbal language and understanding facial and body language. They act and speak impulsively and because they may be agitated by their current situation, will try to tell you everything at once. He or she can be helped by:

10. Being clear in your speech and intention and talking calmly
11. Asking single questions that are not leading along a predetermined pathway

12. Avoiding unnecessarily repetitious, irrelevant or confusing questions
13. Breaking up the questions asked (in interview, at any appointment or in court) into predetermined time scales, such as background history, what happened immediately before the event, what happened at the event and what happened after the event. Further subdividing the questions into those that relate to the interviewee and then again for others who may have been involved, i.e. ask the questions differently according to the intended recipient.

A person with ADHD, talking about an issue, may very well wander off the track and leave the situation confused. He or she may be helped by:

14. Allowing him or her to practice what they want to say in advance of doing so.

People with ADHD are prone to exaggerating any story to improve their own part in it. This is to counteract their very low self-esteem, but can of course implicate them deeply in something that they had either no part or only a minor part in. He or she can be helped by:

15. Careful questioning to accurately gauge the extent of their involvement.

What about sentencing those with ADHD; what should be considered?

In any case the court's task on sentence is, through a process of reasoning, to make an order (or orders) which is:

• A proportionate response to the persistence and seriousness of the offending
• Is an intervention which in its judgement tackles the factors associated with the child or young person's offending behaviour and is most likely to prevent further offending
• Has proper regard to the offender's welfare

The process involves answering a number of core questions:

The offence

How serious is the offence? Does anything aggravate it? Are there any associated offences to consider? Does anything mitigate it? Is it a sexual or violent offence? Is there a serious risk of harm to the public?

The offender

What are the circumstances of the offender, including any mitigating factors? What welfare issues are there?

The options

• Is the court required to impose a specific order e.g. referral order?
• What is the risk of this young person offending again? What intervention should the court consider; what in their judgement, based on all the

evidence and reports (including views expressed by the offender and his or her parents) is most likely to prevent this particular young person from offending again?

- Is the intervention which the court has in mind, an appropriate punishment in the sense of being proportionate to the seriousness and persistence of his or her offending behaviour? Are the thresholds for community sentence/custody met?

The order

Subject to proportionality (seriousness) and welfare (where there are specific issues), is the order the best option for preventing re-offending?

In this process, the fact that the defendant has ADHD is one of a number of factors to be considered. It is certainly relevant to those questions relating to the offender, the options and the order.

In this regard it is interesting to note that those with ADHD are **accustomed to punishment**. Because of the nature of ADHD they will have been *getting it wrong* in every way, all of their lives; not necessarily in a criminal way but probably in every other way!

They will have been punished consistently all of their lives and become more and more accepting of it. It is hard to punish someone who **expects** to be punished and **adapts** to whatever penalty is given.

It goes without saying that if, having regard to its task and answers to the core questions outlined above, the order of the court for a defendant with ADHD requires a punitive element then one should be imposed. Having said that in relation to the specific orders available to the Youth Court it can be observed that:

- **Fines, costs and compensation:**
  The general principle that parents or guardians have responsibility for the payment of financial orders remains. Having said that if the parent also suffers from this disorder he or she will, along with other problems, have great difficulty managing money. They will invariably be using some form of addictive material to self medicate be it cigarettes, alcohol or cannabis and any money they have will first be used for this. Memory difficulties will also conspire to ensure that fines are not remembered
- **Reparation, action plan, attendance centre, supervision, curfew, community rehabilitation, community punishment, community punishment and rehabilitation and drug treatment and testing Orders:**
  These will have a beneficial effect on the offender. An order might specifically recognise that he or she has ADHD and provide the sort of structured intervention that would help to alleviate its problems. It may provide an opportunity for the offender to seek out regular medical help from professionals experienced in their disorder. It could give them access

81

to a Counsellor or Community Psychiatric Nurse who would help them maintain any contact regimes and ensure that they are receiving help with impulsive anger management and taking appropriate medication.

However, as indicated, those with ADHD lack organisation skills and have difficulties keeping appointments. They will either be two hours early or two hours late: that is if they remember at all! They often set out for an appointment at the time they should be there. Or they will arrive on time but on the wrong day!

- **Detention and training orders:**
  The Detention element can give the structure and security that someone with ADHD will crave **BUT** it could be a harsh environment in which they may not receive medication. The training element would again be beneficial to the offender if it provided the same sort of structured intervention relating to Community Penalties.

So, in a nutshell

ADHD is not easy; it's not easy for the carers, parents or teachers that assist young people with ADHD. It's certainly not easy to run an effective court when there is a witness or defendant who has ADHD. But spare an additional thought. Having ADHD is not easy either.

With forethought and special considerations where appropriate, the chances of a successful rehabilitation for a person with ADHD who is an offender can be greatly increased.

ADHD should never be used to excuse anyone's behaviour, but it may well explain someone's behaviour, if we are prepared to listen.

Resources and Support

ADDISS

(The national Attention Deficit Disorder Information and Support Service)
Room 201 Premier House
Edgware
Middx
HA8 7BJ

Registered charity no 1070827

Tel No: 0208 952 2800
E-Mail: info@addiss.co.uk
Website: www.addiss.co.uk

ADDISS can provide you with a list of groups across the UK and Scotland including its 26 affiliate groups

Websites based in the UK

www.adders.org
A large website offering discussion boards, news items and a list of over 40 support groups around the world

www.mkadhd.org.uk
The Milton Keynes group website offering lots of information on ADHD and support
+ 44-01908 675110

Other useful contacts in the UK

ACE Advisory Centre for Education
Gives advice on exclusions and other education issues
General Advice Line 0808 8005793
Exclusion Advice Line 0808 8000327
Website: www.ace-ed.org.uk

Mind
Support Tel: 08457 660 163
Website: www.mind.org.uk

Young Minds
Support Tel: 0800 018 2138
Website: www.youngminds.org.uk

Action for Prisoners' Families
Support Tel: 0808 808 2003 (Dedicated helpline)
Office Tel: 0208 812 3600
Fax: 0208 871 0473
Email: info@actionpf.org.uk
Website: www.prisonersfamilies.org.uk

The Howard League for Penal Reform
Tel: +44 (0)20 7249 7373
Email: info@howardleague.org
Website: www.howardleague.org

NACRO
(National Association for the Care and Resettlement of Offenders)
Support Tel: 0800 0181 259 (Dedicated helpline)
Email: helpline@nacro.org.uk
Website: www.nacro.org.uk

NIACRO
Support Tel: 028 9032 0157/
028 7126 4555
Email: niacro@niacro.co.uk
Website: www.niacro.co.uk

Parentline Plus
Support Tel: 0808 800 2222
Website: www.parentlineplus.org.uk

www.hmprisonservice.gov.uk
HM Prison Service The prison service for England and Wales website giving news and updates plus useful information on every prison establishment in England and Wales.

www.homeoffice.gov.uk
The Home Office is the government department responsible for internal affairs in England and Wales

www.justask.org.uk
Directory of Legal Services Commission
Quality Marked organisations and
solicitors offering advice to the public
in England & Wales.

www.prisonreformtrust.org.uk
Prison Reform Trust Website contains
news and current projects and events,
publications list, details and subscrip-
tion information for Prison Report
magazine. Prisoners' advice and
information. Links and list of useful
organisations.

www.sps.gov.uk
Scottish Prison Service

www.sps.gov.uk
Scottish Prisoners' Families Helpline
offers information and support to anyone with a relative or friend in prison.
Freephone number 0500 83 93 83 or
see www.familiesoutside.org.uk

www.womeninprison.org.uk
Women in Prison A support and cam-
paigning group for women prisoners.

Support and Resources outside the UK

Australia
Learning Difficulties Coalition NSW
www.learningdifficultiescoalition.org.au

Austria
Verein Adapt
www.adapt.at

Belgium
www.tdah.be
www.zitstil.be

Cyprus
ADD-ADHD Support Cyprus
www.add-adhd.org.cy

Denmark
Verein Adapt
www.adapt.at

Germany
ADHS Deutschland i.G
www.adhs-deutschland.de

Ireland
HADD
www.hadd.ie

Italy
AIFA Onlus (Associazione Italiana
Famiglie ADHD)
http://www.aifa.it

Netherlands
Impuls
http://www.impulsdigitaal.nl

Norway
ADHD Norge
http://www.adhd-foreningen.no

Poland
Polish ADHD Association
www.ptadhd.pl

Spain
Fundación Adana
www.f-adana.org
Federacion Española de Asociaciones
de Ayuda al Deficit de Atencion e
Hiperactividad
www.feaadah.org

Sweden
Riksförbrudet Attention
www.attention-riks.se

Russia
The Vnimanie Foundation
www.vnimanie.org

USA
CHADD
Children and Adults with Attention
Deficit Hyperactivity Disorder
Tel +1 301 -306 -7070
www.chadd.org

ADDA
Attention Deficit Disorder Association
www.add.org